In memory of

MIKE POTE

Contents

Figure list

Tables

Acknowledgement

Mike Pote led the Project Management team within the NHS Management Executive's Resource Management Unit until his death in 1991. He was a friend and colleague who is sadly missed. Since he was always encouraging members of the team to write down and share their knowledge and experiences, this book would seem a fitting tribute.

A number of people were kind enough to read through a draft of the manuscript and offer their comments; without this help the book could not have been completed. Thanks go to Mr Steve Dent of TDS, Mr Peter Jackson of Huddersfield Health Authority, Mr Vic Peel of the Health Services Management Unit in Manchester, Dr Jenny Simpson, Chief Executive of the British Association of Medical Managers (BAMM) and my colleague and fellow Director of Health Strategies, Mr Tim Scott.

1. Introduction

The management of quality and cost is high on the agenda of most clinical and general managers these days. The aim of those purchasing health care for the local population is to ensure high quality care at a reasonable and affordable cost. The debate will continue as to what is meant by 'high', 'reasonable' and 'affordable', but most will agree that funds are limited and that difficult decisions need to be made as to the numbers and types of patients and the nature of the care and treatment provided. The aim of providers is to ensure that high quality care is provided. It is important that this can be provided at a price that is attractive to the local purchasers; particularly in those areas where there are choices that can be made between providers. Purchasers are concerned to ensure that they are comparing like with like when considering the value for money obtained from different providers.

Quality and cost are not in opposition. Evidence shows that high quality care costs less than poor quality care. 'Getting it right first time', having fewer avoidable complications and eliminating unnecessary interventions while providing better clinical outcomes and improving patient satisfaction all contribute to improved quality at lower cost.

Quality and cost can only be managed if they can be measured and if the desired levels can be described against which achievements can be compared. Over recent years, all large acute hospitals have invested in systems which can do just this: the Casemix Management system. These systems provide information to support, measure and record the treatment given to patients, and the cost of providing that service. This information supports the processes by which the services provided are managed: medical and clinical audit, business planning, contracting, internal trading, and budgeting. The basis of the information is the individual patient, the reason for their contact with the health services, the services they receive, the resources they consume and, potentially, the outcome of that care. In this way all the main management processes are directly linked to the clinical care of the patient.

This book has been written primarily to help clinical and general managers in hospitals to understand and exploit the potential of the information available to them; to enable them to better understand the quality and cost of care provided, to use this information effectively to support the main management processes of the hospital and to obtain the maximum benefit from the investment already made in management information systems. It will be of interest to clinicians and others involved in medical and clinical audit programmes. It will be of use to clinical directors, business managers, nurse managers, corporate managers in finance, operations, contracting and marketing who are involved in the management processes.

While most hospitals have procured management information systems which have the potential to provide all the information discussed in this book, most hospitals are not exploiting this potential to its full. This book describes some of the organisational and technical reasons why this is so, and how they may be overcome. It will therefore be of interest to those involved in the provision of information and information systems as well as those who use the information.

The focus is on the availability and use of information in managing quality and cost within acute hospitals although the principles apply to others providers of health care.

Purchasers of health care will be interested in the information that is available to the providers of that care. They will be interested in the information transfer that may be negotiated as part of the contracting process; information that can reduce the risk of the contracting process to both providers and purchasers.

The principal information system referred to is called a Casemix Management system. The name implies to some, quite erroneously, that its main use is to manage the mix of cases within a hospital. The name actually arises from the fact that the mix of cases is taken into account in the analysis and presentation of information.

Some hospitals have now had patient-based information systems in place for some years. Most are obtaining some benefit from their investment; all could obtain much more. It is easy for optimists to say that it is too early to expect the benefits and to wait to see if benefits arise; this is true, but benefits will not necessarily arise. It is also easy for them to say that the system needs further development and to wait to see if developments occur; it is true, but developments will not necessarily occur. Pessimists may be more inclined to consider that those benefits are not available and abandon the effort made so far. It is more difficult to accept that systems can and will yield benefits but that action must be taken to ensure that it happens. This book explains the issues and methods for tackling benefits realisation.

Chapter 2. Managing with information

This chapter describes the philosophy behind the Casemix Management system introduced into acute hospitals. It describes the principal structures and how it is possible to use these to link clinical activity to the main management processes.

Chapter 3. Supporting clinical and general management processes

This chapter gives practical examples of information that can promote a better understanding of the quality and cost of care. It shows some ways in which information can be used to support various management processes, including audit, planning, budgeting and contracting. All Casemix Management systems procured under the NHS Management Executive's resource management programme and conforming to the minimum requirements stated by that programme can do what is shown here, and more. It might look very different to your casemix system but your system is capable of providing the same information. It is hoped that these ideas will give rise to many others. Where examples draw on data which might not be found in a basic system, this is pointed out.

Chapter 4. Implementing management information

The level of benefits that can be obtained from an information system depend not only on the system itself and the way it is designed but also on the way it is implemented and used within a particular hospital. Many of the early sites have, with hindsight, implemented their systems in such a way that it will only be possible to obtain limited benefits from them. This chapter discusses the management issues (not technical issues) which are concerned in the implementation and on which the uses to which the information can be put depend. Methods for identifying and realising the benefits of management information systems are discussed.

Chapter 5. Describing patients and processes

The information about patients and what happens to them is obtained from a variety of sources and much of this data is coded. A key to the linking of clinical and management processes is the complete and accurate clinical coding of patient records. This chapter discusses issues concerning that data and the way it is obtained and coded.

Chapter 6. Patient-based management information systems

The main patient-based information system required to support the objectives of resource management is the Casemix Management system. The origins, nature, content and major differences in approach of systems on the market are described. The full range of support may be provided by a sophisticated Casemix Management system alone or a more basic system used in conjunction with Audit systems. The requirements for an integrated solution are discussed and how these may be provided by a number of approaches.

Chapter 7. Care profiles

A key feature of the information and its ability to underpin the hospital in its objectives is the care profile, defining the expected process of care for a group of patients, which might be expected to elicit a similar clinical response and consume similar resources. Profiles describe the expected quality and cost of the care process for these clinically coherent groups of patients. This chapter discusses various issues concerning the definition and use of care profiles and their distinction from care or treatment protocols.

Chapter 8. Costing

Within a patient-based system, costs are used for two distinct purposes: to provide a common means of describing activity measured in different terms (e.g. pathology tests and nursing hours) and to be the basis for exchange of real money through the budgeting, contracting and internal trading processes. The principles, nature, source and use of cost information are discussed.

Chapter 9. Reporting

The information system described is basically a large repository of data which can be analysed and presented in an infinite number of ways. This data needs to be analysed and presented to clinicians and managers in a form that assists them in their tasks and is provided as and when they require it. This demands a high quality reporting system, including capabilities for a variety of output formats, including graphics, which is described in this chapter and of which examples are given.

Chapter 10. Identifying and realising benefits

No one has to use management information. It will only be used if it is of personal benefit. This involves understanding what is available and how it can be applied to a particular individual's responsibilities. This chapter discusses aspects of training and development required within a hospital if the information becoming available is to be used effectively to improve patient care. It discusses available benefits and how these can be realised. It discusses the development of an information culture within a hospital as well as the technical skills required by selected individuals.

   The management of any organisation is primarily about people, their attitudes and behaviour. This book describes how information can be used to support management processes. It addresses some of the techniques that can be used to identify and realise benefits. Clinical and general managers must not only have convenient access to appropriate information and know how to use that information, they must also perceive some direct personal benefit in the use of that information. This is more easily achieved if those who will use the information are directly involved in any decisions regarding the information and information system that provides it.

2. Managing with information

Introduction

Hospitals are complex organisations which have a range of roles. They are responsible for treating acute illnesses and trauma, treating and supporting those with chronic illnesses, promoting healthy lifestyles, training health professionals and playing an active role in the cultural life of the local community. Providing facts and figures about the hospital reduces this rich diversity and involves categorising activities and individuals into groups, which requires a degree of simplification and generalisation. This is necessary because if you can't measure what is happening, then you can't manage it. Managing quality and cost depends on understanding what factors affect these items, being able to measure these factors, setting targets that we wish to achieve, and being able to monitor progress towards these targets.

Collecting data and producing information is a costly process in its own right and must be justified on the benefits it brings to individuals and the organisation as a whole. The minimum amount of data must therefore be collected to support the widest range of purposes. In order to achieve this we create a simplified model of the hospital; one that reflects those essential elements of a hospital which allow us to manage.

This chapter describes the model that is used as the basis for current hospital management information systems; the model that underpins an understanding of how the information may be used and the limitations that it imposes.

Model of a hospital

In essence, the process of health care can be stated as patients with need demand services which consume resources and result in outcomes. Patients have conditions (problems, symptoms or diagnoses) and a prognosis. Health care processes are packages of resource use (consultations, investigations, treatments) which combine in episodes of care.[1]

This gives us the building blocks for our model. If the information is to be of use to clinical or general management it must address:

- The patients the hospital treats and the reason for their treatment.
- Resources used by the patients and the associated cost of these resources.

- Quality of care received by each patient: the care process, its outcome and the satisfaction of the patient with the care they received.

In order to link clinical and management processes and ensure that the resulting information is able to support a wide range of processes, the relationship between each of these factors needs to be investigated. This is achieved through a model based on the main focus of the hospital itself: the patient.

Group	Description
D01	Chest procedures - category 6
D02	Chest procedures - category 4
D03	Chest procedures - category 2
D05	Respiratory procedures - category 5
D06	Respiratory procedures - category 4
D07	Respiratory procedures - category 3
D08	Pulmonary embolus - died
D09	Pulmonary embolus - secondary to procedure
D10	Pulmonary embolus - other
D11	Bronchoscopy - rigid
D12	Bacterial respiratory infection - with complex diagnoses
D13	Bacterial respiratory infection - without complex diagnoses
D14	Respiratory infection - TB
D15	Other respiratory infection - non-viral pneumonia
D16	Other respiratory infection - viral pneumonia
D19	Other respiratory infection - cystic fibrosis
D20	Other respiratory infection - bronchiectasis
D21	Chronic obstructive airways disease - with assisted ventilation
D22	Chronic obstructive airways disease - other
D23	Asthma
D25	Other respiratory infections - brochiolitis, bronchitis
D30	Respiratory neoplasms
D31	Pleural effusion - malignant with pleural tap/biopsy
D32	Pleural effusion - malignant other
D33	Pleurisy / pleural effusion - without malignancy
D34	Interstitial lung disease
D35	Pulmonary oedema
D36	Pneumothorax - traumatic
D37	Pneumothorax - complex
D38	Pneumothorax - simple
D39	Other respiratory disease

Table 1. Respiratory groups

While it is recognised that each patient is an individual and the treatment or care they receive will be tailored to their individual requirements, in order to manage, to predict and plan for the future, it is necessary to identify similarities between patients and their treatment.

The model used is based on the concept of individual patients who can be placed in groups which are defined by clinical characteristics. All patients within a single group will use similar packages of services. The clinical activities of a hospital can be described in a limited number of such groups of patients. Experience suggests that the majority of inpatients of a general hospital will be covered by 200–250 groups. The groups are homogeneous in that each patient within a group elicits a similar clinical response and would therefore be expected to consume similar resources.

A number of classification systems exist for describing such groups, for example Diagnosis Related Groups (DRGs), Healthcare Resource Groups (HRGs) and Ambulatory Visit Groups (AVGs). Table 1 lists the respiratory groups from the HRG classification for hospital inpatients. Groups are described in more detail in Chapter 5.

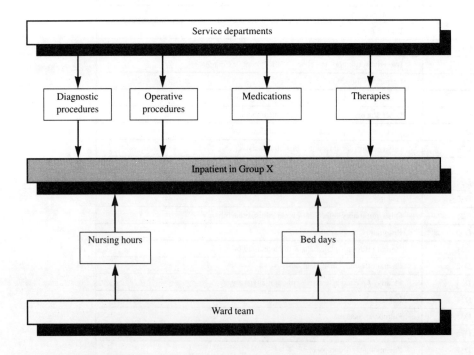

Figure 1. Patient group

For each group, the expected package of services can be described in a profile for that group. For example, the expected diagnostic tests, operative procedures, therapies, Figure 1. Patient group medications, bed days, nursing hours, etc., can be described. These will be described either in absolute terms, for example 'one operation', or in statistical terms, for example '60 per cent of the group have one operation'.

Figure 1 shows a patient in Group X. The diagnostic procedures, bed days, etc., are packages of services received by that patient, each contributing to the total care of the patient.

A set of profiles covering all patients treated or cared for by the hospital, linked to the expected numbers of patients in each group, gives the expected or planned activity of the hospital. This activity can be aggregated to give a view for the hospital as a whole or disaggregated to give a view for the various organisational entities within the hospital, for example Clinical Directorates, Service Departments, or external entities, for example purchasers.

The profile can be extended to describe not only the expected process of care, but also the expected outcome for a patient within the group. This is limited only by the current

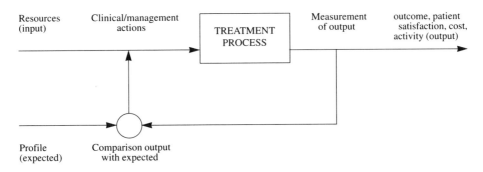

Figure 2. General control diagram

ability to be able to define outcomes.

Actual patient activity is compared to the relevant profile and gives rise to variations from what was planned or expected. This may be for an individual patient whose care varied from that expected or for groups of patients. There may be more or less patients in a particular group than expected (volume variation), they may have had more or less events than expected (process variation) or the proportions of patients across the groups may vary (casemix variation). This again may be viewed for the hospital as a whole or disaggregated to give a view for the various organisational entities.

Each activity within the profile or actual patient activity can be costed. Just as the total expected activity of the hospital can be identified from the content of the profiles and the expected number of patients in each group, so can the expected cost.

Figure 2 shows:

- how the resources used in the treatment process,
- resulting in outcomes for the patient,
- can be compared to expectations,
- which identify variations and lead to clinical or management action,
- to modify the process, the resources or the expectations.

While most of the early work related to acute inpatients, the model is equally applicable to outpatients and day patients. This is particularly important for those specialties where the majority of patient care takes place in these settings.

Information based on the model

The management processes of the organisation are linked to the direct clinical activity through information systems based on this model. Contracts and budgets can be negotiated on the basis of the patients that are expected to be treated and the clinical activity expected to be involved with each patient. The quality of the care process and outcomes can be monitored on a regular basis through the audit process. Everyone uses the same model of the hospital to support both clinical and general management processes. The information which is used throughout derives from the clinical process. While aggregate information will be used to support most of the general management processes, it is always possible to track back to the individual patients and details of their treatment where this is necessary.

The data is derived from operational systems. That is, from systems where there is direct benefit to those recording the data to ensure that it is accurate. For example, nurses on the ward assessing and recording patient dependency or doctors coding the medical diagnosis.

The model described is the basis for the audit and Casemix Management systems in hospitals today.

This patient-based model allows a better understanding of how resources are used to provide high quality care to individual and groups of patients and it provides a better understanding of those factors which directly influence the use of resources and hence the cost of providing services. It has often been argued that, particularly in medical specialties, where the majority of cases are emergencies, there is little control over either the casemix or the number of cases. However, we can understand the use of resources for particular types of patients and predict the numbers in each group. We can therefore plan provision of appropriate resources, negotiate advantageous contracts with purchasers, ensure income to cover costs and predict the impact of anticipated changes in demography or medical advances even where the factors are not directly under the control of the hospital.

It is not unreasonable to expect that planning the work that the hospital expects to undertake (that is the contracts it wishes to negotiate), is based on the clinical requirements of the patients and the capacity offered by the available resources: staff time, skills and the more fixed resources such as theatre time. The contracts that can be negotiated, including the numbers of patients to be treated, will depend on the requirements of the purchasers and the cost and quality offered by the hospital. Having negotiated and agreed contracts, the income for the hospital will be defined and the hospital will be committed to treating an agreed number of patients. Within the hospital, the expected numbers of patients are then adjusted in accordance with agreed contracts and form the basis for monitoring throughout the contract period. It might also seem reasonable that, having agreed contracts, budgets are negotiated and agreed on the basis of clinical activity anticipated to be required to fulfil the contracts.

There is a note of caution to sound if the quality (or at least quantity) of the treatment process is not to suffer. Treatment process, number of patients and cost are inseparable (see Figure 3). If any two of these elements are fixed, then the other is automatically defined. For example, if during the contract process the cost (or price) and the number of patients are fixed, then the process must vary if the overall terms of the contract are to be met. Any significant reduction in price or increase in numbers can lead to a detrimental impact on the treatment process or contracts not fulfilled.

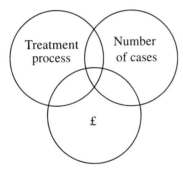

Figure 3. Process, number of cases and cost relationship

3. Supporting clinical and general management processes

Introduction

This chapter gives examples of information and how it can be used to support a range of management processes. The examples are based on the information that is available from a basic Casemix Management system. This is a patient-based information system that meets the minimum requirements as published by the Resource Management Unit of the NHS Management Executive in January 1989.[2] This document gives a list of the minimum data set for Casemix Management systems. The original publication contained those data items relating to inpatients. In Appendix A, the minimum data set has been updated to include additional data items required as a result of the changed management structures and processes resulting from the implementation of the White Paper *Working for Patients,* and now includes data for other types of patients.

Any of the systems that meet the minimum core specification have the potential to provide the type of reports presented here. Because the tools used for reporting vary from system to system, the exact presentation of the information will vary. While the systems have the potential, they may not have been implemented in such a way that they deliver this information. Chapter 4 investigates some of these implementation issues.

The results of a survey published in 1994 identified 15 that met the minimum requirements, Casemix Management Systems Survey.[3] The report is confidential within the NHS and was distributed to Resource Management project managers, Regional Resource Management co-ordinators and others on request.

If you have or are procuring one of the systems described in the report, they can present information in the manner shown and much more besides. Other systems may do so.

Use of information is also dependent on the stage of implementation and the information skills of those using the system. Questions such as 'What does this hospital do?', 'How do they do it?' and 'What does it cost?' can be investigated at an early stage as can some support for audit studies. Linking information to the contracting process can commence as soon as sufficient records are held to cover particular contracts. Full support to audit, contracting, and monitoring activity and cost depend on having a set of agreed groups and profiles for these groups. These are unlikely to be defined until sufficient historical data is available on which to base their definition and test their coherence. Use of the information to support internal trading or budgeting requires a level of completeness in recording both patients and events and will be one of the later processes supported by patient-based information.

It is important to remember in the following cases that the information is merely presented. There is no judgement as to whether the information presented is 'good' or 'bad'. It is for those with the detailed knowledge of the circumstances to interpret the information and determine whether any action is appropriate and what that action should be. As always the information raises yet more questions rather than providing all the answers.

Reporting individual patient records

The patient-based management information system brings together details of all patient activities. Unless your hospital has a fully integrated Hospital Information Support System (HISS), this is likely to be the only integration of all patient events other than the written record. The information will be summarised but gives pointers to where more detailed information may be found.

Patient id	Name	Date of birth	District of residence
198374	Smith, Aaron	12/01/1934	Eastfield
127456	Smith, Anne	09/07/1922	Eastfield
271546	Smith, Anne	03/11/1952	Eastfield
199433	Smith, Aubrey	10/02/1941	Northmoor
278199	Smith, Audrey	18/05/1947	Westbrook
238911	Smith, Beatrice	23/01/1915	Eastfield
166379	Smith, Bernard	30/08/1946	Eastfield
187265	Smith, Caroline	27/02/1936	Eastfield
173480	Smith, Charles	11/06/1929	Southmarsh
129288	Smith, Charles	13/08/1963	Eastfield
194726	Smith, Corrine	22/12/1940	Westbrook

Table 2 Identifying patients

The patient record is the basis for all the reports presented here. All activity and cost is built up from the activity and cost of individual patients. All activity and cost can be tracked down to the individual patient record if necessary. When supporting medical or clinical audit, it is important to be able to identify those patients who are exceptional. It is the management information system that will be used to identify these exceptions and to indicate where further details of the patient may be found.

Patient id	Name	Episode sequence	Type	Start date	Main problem/diagnosis
166379	Smith, Bernard	1	A/E	24 Feb 1993	Abdominal pain
166379	Smith, Bernard	2	I/P	24 Feb 1993	Appendicitis without peritonitis

Table 3. Identifying episodes of care

Patient id	Name	Main problem/diagnosis
166379	Smith, Bernard	Appendicitis without peritonitis
Admitted	24 Feb 1993	
Admitted as	Emergency	
Discharged	03 Mar 1993	
Length of stay	5 days	
Sex	Male	
Age	45	
Contract	Appendicitis	Main purchaser / cost & volume
Resources	Activity	Cost (£)
Major theatre	1.0 hour	226.00
Simple radiology	1 film	10.80
Simple biochemistry	1 test	3.80
Simple haematology	3 tests	10.50
Simple histology	1 test	3.20
Simple microbiology	1 test	4.20
Pharmacy	38 doses	45.60
Qualified nursing	11 hours	110.00
Unqualified nursing	5 hours	45.60
Other services	1 hour	4.00
Length of episode	5 days	25.00
Total		488.70

Table 4 Details of episode

A much simplified version of the available information is presented for the sake of brevity in Tables 2, 3 and 4. Full dates and descriptions of all individual events are available on the patient record.

Describing the work of the hospital

In the following examples, the information is used to answer the questions:

- What does this hospital do?
- What does it cost?

A great variety of information is available to describe the work of the hospital. Just a few examples of the information are presented here. Most users of the information will require a series of structured reports, on a regular basis, linked to their role, responsibilities and interests within the hospital.

Much of this information is available from other sources and has been available for a number of years but it has been hard to get at and difficult to display in a consistent format.

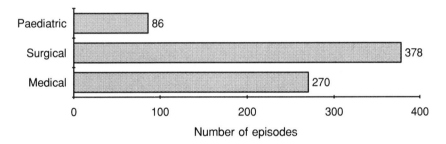

Figure 4. Episodes by clinical team

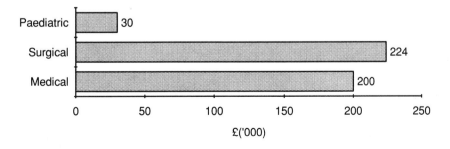

Figure 5. Costs by clinical team

15

The information in Figures 4-13 relates to a fictitious hospital. The numbers of clinical teams, specialties and consultants have been much reduced from those you would find in a typical general hospital. Activity information is given for hospital inpatients treated over a month within the hospital.

Figures 4 and 5 show the number of inpatient episodes and cost incurred for each of the three clinical teams within the hospital.

We might want to see how this cost is distributed across the service departments within the hospital, as shown in Figure 6.

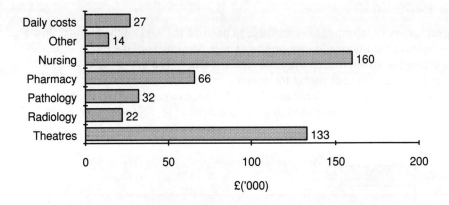

Figure 6. Cost by service department

Or by purchasers of health care, Figure 7.

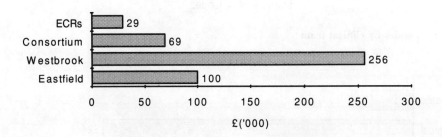

Figure 7. Cost by purchaser

Managers within a clinical team will want to have a series of reports that are about the activity within their own team. The number of inpatient episodes for each specialty in the team is shown in Figure 8, followed by the cost shown in Figure 9.

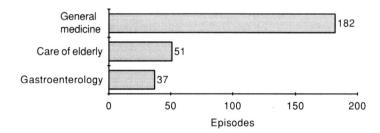

Figure 8. Inpatient activity by specialty

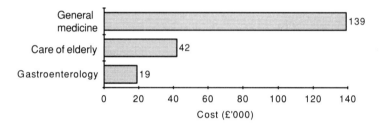

Figure 9. Inpatient cost by specialty

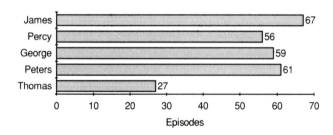

Figure 10. Inpatient episodes by consultant

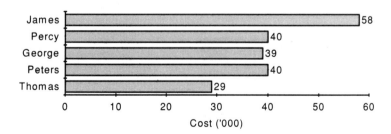

Figure 11. Inpatient costs by consultant

Figures 10 and 11 show the activity and cost incurred by individual consultants within a clinical team.

A manager of the clinical team might be interested in why Dr Thomas, being responsible for ten per cent of the inpatient activity, incurred 14.5 per cent of the costs. Could it be because Dr Thomas' cases were more complex, requiring more, or more costly, resources? Figure 12 shows the mix of cases for the period in question for the clinical team as a whole and could be analysed for each consultant. The small numbers of episodes and the very different type of cases shown in this figure should make it obvious why information adjusted for the mix of cases might avoid misunderstandings of information which shows apparent anomalies but may be easily explained when that mix is taken into account.

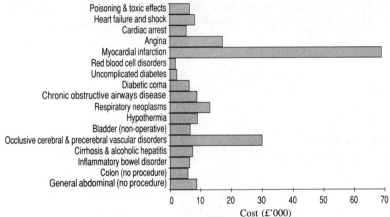

Figure 12. Cost implication of patient groups

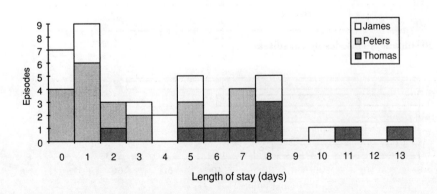

Figure 13. Length of stay distribution of angina patients for different consultants

We might want to look in greater depth at a particular group and the resources that are being used. Figure 13 shows the length of stay for angina patients and how this varies for different consultants.

It has only been possible to show some of the reports that are available to describe what the hospital does and what it costs.

Implications of changing numbers of patients and patterns of care

A common requirement is to predict the implications on each individual department of an expected change in the numbers of patients, or ways in which they are treated. This may arise in any number of circumstances but common ones would be the introduction of a new service, discontinuing a service, changes in casemix due to changes in the contracts negotiated with purchasers or an increase in a particular group, perhaps as part of a waiting list initiative. In each case the basic process is the same.

We start with a simple example of an expected increase in one particular patient group. Table 5 shows the activity implications of carrying out 50 cases of primary replacement of major joints. In this example, other variables are held constant and resource constraints ignored.

Primary replacement of major joints		
	1 case	50 cases
Stay	19 days	950 days
Major theatres	1.5 hours	75 hours
Pharmacy	345 doses	17,250 doses
Simple biochemistry	7 tests	350 tests
Simple haematology	7 tests	350 tests
Simple histology	1 test	50 tests
Simple microbiology	7 tests	350 tests
Qualified nursing	29 hours	1,450 hours
Unqualified nursing	28 hours	1,400 hours
Other services	50 hours	2,500 hours

Table 5. Calculating the activity implications of more cases

The activity for one case is that which is defined on the care profile for primary replacement of major joints and is shown here in broad grouping of service departments. More precise information would be available within clinical level profiles but for managing resources over a range or all casemix groups this level of detail is appropriate.

When considering a change in the treatment of a group of patients, it may be desirable to define two profiles, one for the current treatment process and a second for the treatment being considered. The impact on different services can be identified by calculating the effect of both using the same number of patients in the group for each profile.

Be cautious about converting this activity implication to a cost implication. Casemix Management systems use standard costs for individual events. The standard costs for many events are dependent on the level of activity. For example, a large increase in the requirement for pathology tests may require additional staff or equipment. This affects the fixed costs of the Pathology department which may increase the standard cost of tests. However, if spare capacity exists in the Pathology department, an increase in activity may be at marginal cost, hence only affecting the variable cost element of the standard cost.

In this example, one group of patients has been chosen. By defining profiles for each of the patient groups and recording the expected number of patients for each group, the total activity and cost of patient care for the whole hospital, or any part of it, can be identified. The workload of the service departments can be estimated from knowing the types of patients that will be treated, anticipated changes in numbers and anticipated changes in the treatment for these groups.

Monitoring activity, quality and cost

Most managers have a great deal of information that they need to monitor on a regular, monthly basis. It is not the absolute levels that are of concern but how activity, quality and cost has varied from what was intended. In the past, such monitoring has largely been based on changes from what happened last year. Now information is available to monitor what happens against what is intended to happen during the period being monitored.

Not all clinical changes are planned. It is important that unplanned changes are picked up as soon as possible so they can be encouraged or discouraged and the future implications identified. Large amounts of information can be regularly monitored and differences spotted between what was intended and what actually happened.

The definition of profiles for each group of patients and the number of patients in each group is the key to this monitoring.

The following sequence shows how a series of figures and tables might be used to monitor the activity and cost. The information is for a fictitious general hospital. (Source: modified from 'Health Strategies', unpublished) It is six months into the year and the Director of Operations is reviewing the latest cost figures. The actual activity undertaken by the hospital is some £400,000 over budget, based on the standard costs of that activity, Table 6.

Hospital costs (£'000)				
	Medical specialties	Surgical specialties	Other	Total
Actual	6,420	5,500	3,640	15,560
Expected	6,300	5,200	3,660	15,160
Variation	120	300	-20	400
% Variation	2%	6%	-1%	3%

Table 6. Hospital costs by clinical team

A quick look at the graphical output shows that the majority of this overspend is in Surgery, Figures 14 and 15.

Clinical team cost variation

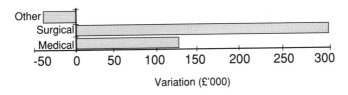

Figure 14. Cost variation by clinical team

Clinical team percentage cost variation

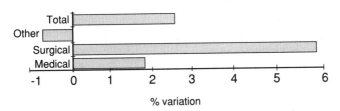

Figure 15. Percentage cost variation by clinical team

The Director of Operations wants to discuss this issue with the Clinical Director of Surgery. The Business Manager had already drawn the attention of the Clinical Director to these figures and to further detail shown by Figures 16-20.

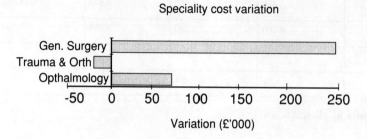

Figure 16. Cost variation, surgical specialties

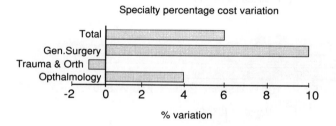

Figure 17. Percentage cost variation, surgical specialties

Figures 16 and 17 suggest the overspend is largely in General Surgery. Ophthalmology is part of the problem and Trauma and Orthopaedics is just about as expected. Further investigation of General Surgery shows where the problem is. Figures 18 and 19 show the use of services by General Surgery.

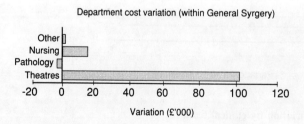

Figure 18. Service cost variation

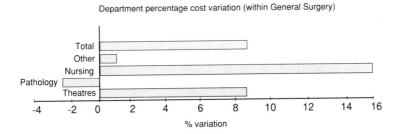

Figure 19. Service percentage cost variation

These figures show nursing costs up 16 per cent and a nine per cent rise in Theatre cost over what was expected. Figure 20 shows the component parts of this variation.

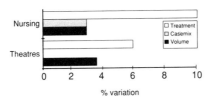

Figure 20. Type of variation

This is showing that three per cent of the variation in cost is due to more patients being treated. The type of cases meant that nursing was increased by three per cent but there was no impact on theatres because of this. The biggest variation is a change in the costs of treating the patients. This is not due to rises in costs since standard costs are used throughout.

Having narrowed down the issue, further detail can be obtained. In Table 7, the groups of patients contributing most to the overspend are investigated. Arterial procedures were for abdominal aortic aneurysm. Appendectomy includes cases with and without peritonitis.

	Arterial procedures	Appendectomy	Other	Total
Actual episodes	35	970	1,240	2,245
Expected episodes	36	974	1,107	2,117
Nursing hours - actual per case	18.1	16.1	9.0	12.2
Nursing hours - expected per case	18.0	16.0	9.0	12.3
Theatre hours - actual per case	2.5	0.9	0.8	0.9
Theatre hours - expected per case	1.6	0.8	0.8	0.8
Average cost per case (£)	3,600	890	480	698
Expected cost per case (£)	1,200	820	450	633
Group cost variation	200%	9%	6%	10%
Volume variation	-5%	-2%	5%	5%
Treatment variation	215%	6%	2%	5%
Total cost implication (£)	82,800	64,620	97,050	244,000

Table 7. Patient groups within General Surgery with cost variation >£50,000

This shows that increased Theatre time for arterial procedures is trebling the cost of this group. For the high volume appendectomies, a little extra nursing and Theatre time soon adds up to a significant amount.

The information is discussed at the next Directorate meeting to make people aware of the impact this is having on the Directorate budget and whether anything can be done. In the meantime, the Clinical Director discusses theatre usage with a consultant who is generally known by his colleagues to be slower than they are. The problem is thought to be with the anaesthetist and discussions with the Directorate responsible for anaesthetics were arranged. A multi-disciplinary group was convened to review the protocol for appendectomies with a view to bringing practice back in line with that agreed with clinicians at the beginning of the year.

This example shows how a great deal of information can be monitored given a number of key indicators. Should a problem be apparent, this can be investigated and narrowed down until the source is found and the required action identified. The information does not give all the answers; it raises further questions, suggests areas for discussion and allows people to make decisions about any actions that should be taken.

The identification of a cost issue, as in this example, is investigated and actions agreed which involve clinicians and take into consideration the quality of clinical care.

Medical and clinical audit

Quality of patient care needs to be incorporated into all clinical and management processes: contracting, budgeting, business planning and general monitoring of activity and cost. This is particularly true through the identification of variations in the processes of patient care and potentially outcome of that care. However, the processes particularly concerned with managing quality of care are those of medical and clinical audit, with some hospitals having wider-ranging quality programmes. 'Total quality management' and 'continuous quality improvement' are just two of the names given to such programmes.

Casemix information can and does provide a great deal of support to medical and clinical audit. As with other processes, the extent to which systems support the audit process depend on their level of sophistication. Some of the systems will allow local tailoring of data items, data items specific to particular specialties to be added locally, or data items to be added for specific surveys. Sophisticated systems can provide the full range of information support to the audit process. The examples shown here only use the data items that would be found in basic systems.

Topic audit

Individual patient records can be extracted using any of the data items on the system. The most common will be to extract cases with a particular diagnosis or combination of

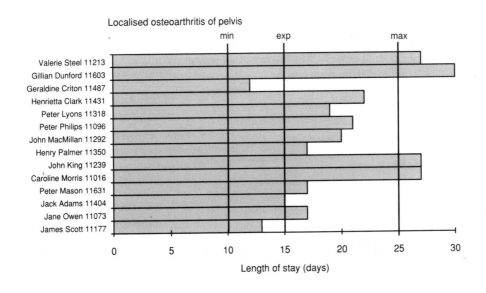

Figure 21. Patient selection for topic audit

diagnoses and patients who had a particular operation. This can be further modified by age, sex, date of episode or any other data item. Patients who have received a particular medication or diagnostic test may need to be identified.

It might be expected that, following extraction of the list of patients, further details are obtained on individual patients either from the system, from operational systems, or from a review of the medical record. For example, the system may well indicate variations in the types of diagnostic tests but identification of variations in the results of those tests may well need access to the physical record.

The example in Figure 21 shows all patients with a particular diagnosis: localised osteoarthritis of pelvis. It shows their individual length of stay in relation to the minimum, maximum and expected length of stay defined on the care profiles.

Instead of length of stay, the item shown might be the use of any other individual resource or an overall indication of process or outcome.

Statistical audit

Certain items, such as post-operative infections or whether a patient is expected to have a particular operation, can only be expressed as a percentage of the group. For example, of a particular group 60 per cent are expected to have operation 1, 30 per cent are expected to have operation 2 and ten per cent are expected to have no operation. A profile can be set which indicates the expected level. The levels actually occurring can be compared against this profile. A distribution of actual patients that varies from the expected can be identified, but not individual patients.

Another technique is to look at the distribution of a particular factor. Figure 22 shows the distribution of length of stay for the patients treated by two consultants. Indicators other than length of stay could be used in a similar manner, as could cost as a general indicator of the overall process. The display of all patient records in a particular casemix group shows up the difference in practice.

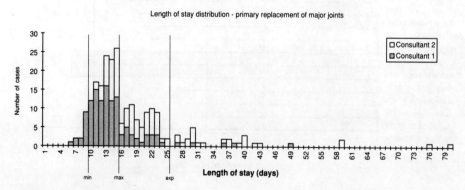

Figure 22. Length of stay distribution

The information tells us that there is a difference between the two consultants, not that either is right or wrong. The variation could result from a number of factors, for example a difference in severity of illness of the patients. Both have patients above the expected and maximum defined lengths of stay. These expected figures will have been defined by the clinicians themselves. The information can lead to an meaningful dialogue as to whether the care was appropriate for the patients included in this group.

In the example shown, it will be of interest to investigate those with length of stay over the maximum. This is a fairly traditional view of quality assurance. However, the aim may be to make improvements for all patients in this group rather than just identify and investigate those outside the target upper limit. Figures 23–25 show how a traditional quality assurance programme and a continuous quality improvement programme might view a significant quality improvement and cost control.

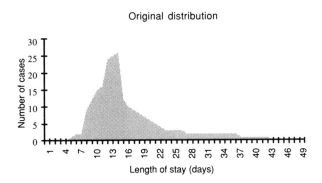

Figure 23. Original length of stay distribution

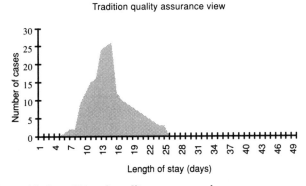

Figure 24. A traditional quality assurance view

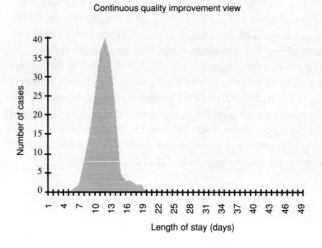

Continuous quality improvement view

Figure 25. Continuous quality improvement view

Identifying outliers

Rather than listing all the patients within a particular group, it is often more convenient to identify only those records which fall outside certain parameters set on the care profile. This can be done for any data item or combination of data items; for example, those patients receiving more or less nursing hours than a defined range, or patients not having the operative procedures expected. Figure 26 is an exception report showing only those records that had a length of stay above the maximum from the previous example shown in Figure 21.

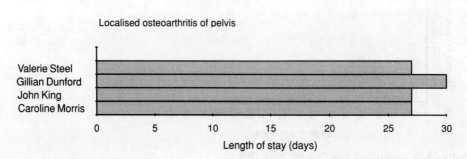

Localised osteoarthritis of pelvis

Figure 26. Identifying outliers

Budgeting and internal trading

Increasingly budgets for service department costs are being held by clinical teams or Directorates. Clinical teams can only control those elements of cost that are directly related to quantity. They have no direct control over fixed costs or overheads; the laboratories, staff and equipment for example. With devolved service budgets, the main clinical teams in effect 'buy' services from departments such as Pathology, Radiology and Theatres.

The purpose of devolving these budgets are many: giving choice to clinical teams as to how they spend their budgets and encouraging efficiency within a service department are just two.

Some hospitals will devolve all of the service department costs to clinical teams, while others will devolve only the variable costs as an initial step. In either case, it is important that the costs of each event can be split into the elements of fixed, semi-variable and variable cost in order to provide a better understanding of the costs incurred and where responsibility for those costs lies. Chapter 8 discusses costs in more detail.

Information now available allows the budget process to be linked directly to the clinical activity expected to be undertaken. Budgets can be based on the cost of expected treatment as defined in profiles and the number of patients expected in each group. The previous monitoring example showed how a variation could be identified as pertaining to a particular Directorate, service department, type or patient group. In a similar way, variations can be identified to particular budget holders and further analysed to indicate to the budget holder the source of that variation.

Table 8 and Figure 27 show how information might be used to distribute pathology costs between the pathology and clinical team budgets. It shows a situation where the fixed costs are provided in a budget held by the Pathology department and the remainder distributed in the budgets of clinical teams. The total pathology budget is £350,000.

Pathology department costs: budget distribution		
Pathology department	£245,000	
Medical team		£55,000
Surgical team		£40,000
Paediatric team		£10,000
Total	£245,000	£105,000

Table 8. Budgets for pathology tests

This figure shows that 70 per cent of pathology costs (£245,000) are included in the pathology budget and the remaining 30 per cent (£105,000) distributed between the three clinical teams on the basis of the number of the tests that they expect to be undertaken on their patients.

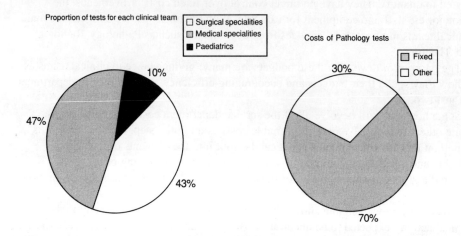

Figure 27. Budgets for pathology tests

The use of information in this manner for linking to budgets assumes that the hospital has made considerable progress in the involvement of clinicians in the management processes and subsequent devolution of budget responsibility to those clinical teams, each accountable for their own elements of the service department budgets. It further assumes significant progress in the implementation of the management information system. It is likely that such use of the information is introduced at an advanced stage of development of devolved management structures and processes.

The use of the Pathology department as the example here raises some interesting issues; for example the numbers of patients that this information relates to. The Pathology department carries out tests not only on hospital patients but patients referred or samples received directly from GPs. Are these patients to be included in the management information system and, if not, what proportion of cost should be allocated against them? This is a choice that is partly dependent on the capabilities of the particular system purchased.

More sophisticated systems have a robust management budgeting module within them. Hospitals with more basic systems will rely on their existing management budgeting systems to provide the reports.

The costs within the Casemix Management system are standard costs. How are these to be reconciled with the actual costs? Again, the sophistication of the system purchased in handling management accounting in relation to the financial accounts is a factor.

Contracting

Contracts with any one purchaser will normally cover a number of different patient groups. For example, a block contract for a specialty covers all patient groups treated within that specialty. Cost and volume contracts, other than those for the high volume groups, will cover a range of groups having different clinical requirements and generating different costs. This makes the risk, carried by the hospital, on any contract particularly vulnerable to changes in the mix of cases presenting. Whether that change of mix is due to the natural variation in case types presenting or due to intended changes by the purchasers, the result is the same: either an underspend or overspend on the contract. It is important that the level of risk on any contract can be determined when new contracts are being planned and that any variation is picked up quickly through a routine monthly monitoring process.

Table 9 shows three ophthalmology groups which might be included within a single contract. The total number of patients is kept the same to show the variation associated solely with the mix of cases. In this example, the number of retinal surgery patients is increased by ten and the number of strabismus surgery patients reduced by ten. This change results in an increased expected cost on the contract of £5,500 or 1.2 per cent.

Ophthalmology contract 1			
Patient group	**Number of cases**	**Expected cost per case**	**Total cost impact (£)**
Estimate 1			
Retinal surgery	100	700	70,000
Lens surgery	1200	300	360,000
Strabismus surgery	300	150	45,000
Total	**1600**		**475,000**
Estimate 2			
Retinal surgery	110	700	77,000
Lens surgery	1200	300	360,000
Strabismus surgery	290	150	43,500
Total	**1600**		**480,500**

Table 9. Effect of changes in casemix on contract costs

In this example, fairly arbitrary changes in the number of patients have been made to model the effect of changes in the mix of patients on the cost of a contract before those contracts are agreed. Analysis of previous casemix within the hospital can provide initial estimates. Statistical techniques can be used to make more robust estimates of the likely variation in numbers of patients within each group and the likely cost variation of actual patients within each group. These figures can then be used to obtain a more accurate level of the risk on each contract. The use of these statistical techniques is beyond the scope of this book.

Of course, there will be many variations in numbers, treatment and mix of cases, many of which will cancel each other out and will not be of concern in the contracting process. It is therefore important that the effect of all the variations can be easily and quickly monitored to identify areas of concern for action to be taken quickly.

Table 10 shows the expected number of cases, cost per case and total cost implications for contracts with one purchaser. In this example, there are two cost and volume contracts and the remainder are block contracts for individual specialties.

Contracts with Purchaser 1				
Contract	Contract type	Expected number of cases	Expected cost per case	Total cost (£'000)
Primary replacement of joints	Cost & volume	110	1715	189
Lens surgery	Cost & volume	925	270	250
Ophthalmology	Block	230	300	69
Trauma & Orthopaedic	Block	715	540	386
General Surgery	Block	1700	410	697
Gastroenterology	Block	530	370	196
Care of the elderly	Block	435	810	352
General Medicine	Block	1610	580	934
Paediatrics	Block	960	240	230
Total		7215		3303

Table 10. Contracts

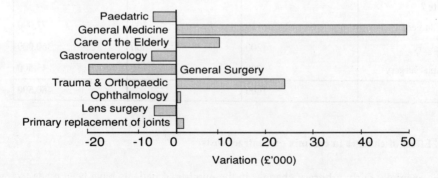

Figure 28. Contract cost variation

The expected number of cases may be spread evenly throughout the year, or may show seasonal variation. Figures 28 and 29 show the total and percentage variation in cost for the first six months of the contracts. The expected number of cases have been adjusted for seasonal variation. Without such adjustment, differences in cost due to numbers of patients and mix could be acted upon in error.

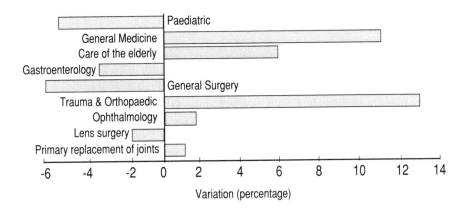

Figure 29. Contract percentage cost variation

In this example, further examination of General Medicine and Trauma and Orthopaedic contracts might well be necessary.

The manner in which the profiles are set up is crucial if the information is to be of use in both the budgeting and contracting processes. By setting up the profiles appropriately, expected and actual activity can be grouped by contract as shown in the previous example. In this way information to manage contracts can be directly linked to the clinical processes. Again the sophistication of the management information system will determine the extent to which this can be done. With a fairly basic system, the information can be used for monitoring of contracts as shown above. The more sophisticated systems will contain a contract management module within them, allowing full monitoring of all contract conditions.

Contracting discussions are not solely based on cost. For example, the health care events, or treatment, that the patient might expect as well as expected outcomes may be included. Treatment and outcome quality standards can be included in profiles and actual levels achieved demonstrated.

Casemix information can indicate:

• The treatment of a patient in each patient group (however that group is defined). For example, the number and nature of pathology tests and nature of operative procedures.

- How this varies from the expected treatment for groups and individual patients (the difference between actual records and the profile).
- The cost of individual patients within each patient group and how this varies from the cost expected had the expected treatment been carried out.
- The health outcome and how this varies from the outcome that might be expected.

Identifying reasons for variation

A powerful feature of Casemix Management systems is that not only can they indicate that what is actually happening varies from what was expected to happen but that the reason for this variation can be identified. A variation at the hospital-wide level can be traced right through to individual patients contributing to that variation. An example of how this might be used to monitor costs was given in the earlier section, Monitoring activity, quality and cost. Table 11 and Figure 30 show how a variation might be tracked from hospital level down to individual specialties and their use of departmental resources.

	Actual	Variation (£'000)
Hospital costs		
Surgical team	224	30
Medical team	170	-13
Paediatrics	30	8
Hospital	424	25
Surgical team costs		
Actual cost (£'000)	224	
Expected cost (£'000)	194	
Variation (£'000)	30	
Variation (percentage)	16	

Table 11. Costs of hospital and clinical teams

The greatest variation in actual cost from that which was expected is in the surgical team, with a variation of £30,000. Table 12 and Figure 31 show how this is split across the different specialties in the team.

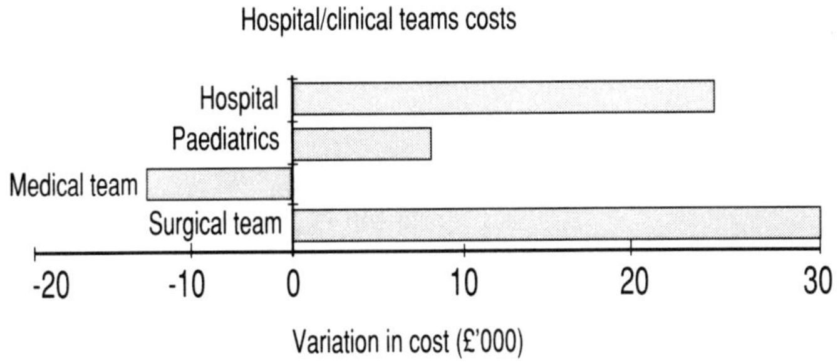

Hospital/clinical teams costs

Hospital
Paediatrics
Medical team
Surgical team

-20   -10   0   10   20   30

Variation in cost (£'000)

Figure 30. Costs of hospital and clinical teams

	Actual	Variation (£'000)
Specialties costs		
Ophthalmology	50	11
Trauma & Orthopaedics	69	-1
General Surgery	105	20
Surgical team	224	30
General Surgery costs		
Actual cost (£'000)	105	
Expected cost (£'000)	85	
Variation (£'000)	20	
Variation (percentage)	24	

Table 12. Costs of surgical team and surgical specialties

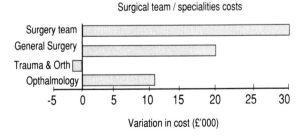

Surgical team / specialities costs

Surgery team
General Surgery
Trauma & Orth
Opthalmology

-5   0   5   10   15   20   25   30

Variation in cost (£'000)

Figure 31. Costs of Surgical team and surgical specialties

General Surgery shows the greatest increase in actual cost over that which was expected, while Trauma and Orthopaedic shows less than expected.

Table 13 and Figure 32 show how the cost of General Surgery was distributed across the use of different departmental resources.

	Actual	Variation (%)
General Surgery costs		
Theatres	46	12
Radiology	4	-1
Pathology	4	0
Pharmacy	12	0
Nursing	33	10
Other	6	-2
General Surgery	105	20

Table 13. Costs of General Surgery and its departmental use

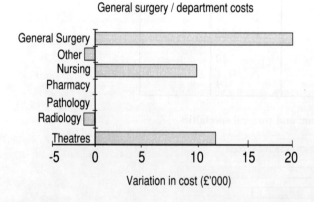

Figure 32. Costs of General Surgery and its departmental use

This shows that the greatest contribution to the variation of costs of General Surgery were in Theatres and Nursing.

At any management level the component parts of the variation can also be identified as to whether it is due to process, volume or casemix. The elements are:

- Treatment variation.
- Volume variation.
- Casemix variation.

A treatment variation occurs when patients have more or less events than were expected for their particular patient group and therefore gives a measure of nature, and potentially the quality of the process of care. For example, they stayed in hospital longer/shorter, had more/less nursing care, more/less pathology tests.

A volume variation occurs when there were more or less patients treated than were expected.

A casemix variation occurs when the type of patient treated varied from the mix that was expected.

Such variations can be calculated in many different ways, all with slightly different meanings. In order to be able to interpret the information correctly, it is important to understand how such variations are calculated within a particular system. Appendix B shows one set of calculations with examples worked over a small number of cases.

Each variation from its corresponding profile is calculated and summed over the total patients and groups covering the management unit or department under consideration. It is not surprising, therefore, that the resulting figures generally present a mix of the different types of variation.

The nature and size of the variation indicates a possible underlying cause and who, within the organisation, is likely to have the responsibility and ability to influence it.

A **treatment variation** is largely controlled by clinical decisions for individual patients. It may also be influenced by level of availability of particular resources. For example, a shortage of Theatre time may result in patients being retained.

It is often argued that a **variation in volume** is largely outside the control of clinicians or managers. There is greater scope for changing volume in those specialties with a higher proportion of elective cases, with volume controlled through the use of waiting lists at various stages of the treatment process. However, the volume can be planned with a high level of accuracy which can be reflected in the contracts that are negotiated. With identification of seasonal variations in volume and good estimating, volume can be controlled within acceptable limits.

As with volume variation, it is also argued that there is little ability to control **casemix variation**. Again there is greater control by clinicians and managers than is often recognised. Variations in mix are largely due to environmental factors but may be due to choices of purchasers or providers to cause a shift in the mix of cases. However, the mix can be predicted with some accuracy, and planned for. It is particularly important to be able to spot quickly those changes which denote a permanent change or drift in the mix of cases. It may be important to identify environmental factors or initiate discussions with purchasers.

Time periods for reporting

As a management information system, it is not generally necessary to report on information at more frequent intervals than monthly. This is not to say that users only require access to the system on a monthly basis. Routine monitoring may well be a monthly exercise, but investigation of particular issues will require the information to be available at any time. If the information is to be used, it must be available to users when they want it. This is not a problem for most Casemix Management systems, which allow 24-hour access and may well extract data from feeder systems on a daily basis.

For monitoring purposes, it is important to know that all the data for a particular period is included in the system and there may well be month-end procedures before routine reports are made available to the users. For example, administrative details of outpatient attendance or patient discharge may be available the day after discharge but it may be some time before the clinical coding is completed.

The basic time period for reporting is the month. If information is to be used to link to budgets and contracts, it is also important that year-to-date information is available. It is also helpful to be able to project the position to the end of the current year. Most systems will not do this automatically but some do and the algorithms necessary can be built into the reporting aspects of any system, if required. Seasonal variation in numbers of patients in different casemix groups affects this projection. A system which allows the expected number of patients in each casemix group for each month will be able to provide more accurate forecasts than one which only allows a single figure for the year. Again systems vary in their abilities in this area. If this forecasting facility is used, it is particularly important to understand how the forecasts have been made in order to be able to interpret the information appropriately. The forecasting feature becomes more useful towards the end of a year when more accurate forecasts can be made.

Other useful time periods to consider are those that allow comparison of what has happened to date this year with what happened last year or what happened this month (or quarter) with what happened in the same period last year. This, of course, implies that the system has been implemented for some time, that data is available and has been managed to be consistent over time. While this is an important feature, it is more likely to be used to address a particular issue or to set numbers of cases or profiles for the following year.

Time periods are:

- Last month.
- Last quarter.
- Last year.
- Year to date.
- Projected end of current year.
- Trend, previous 12 months.
- Same month / quarter last year.

Identifying trends and one-off variations

If information is being monitored on a monthly basis, it is important to be able to distinguish between variation which occurs as one-off events from those which are consistent or demonstrate an increasing or decreasing trend. Even large variation, which is due to a one-off understood and acceptable event, may not require any action. Small variations, which indicate an unacceptable trend, may require urgent action to discourage them. Small variations which indicate an acceptable trend should be encouraged.

4. Implementing management information

Implementation is a management issue

Many implementations of management information systems have a single driving force. For example, clinical aspects or contracting. The system is both installed and implemented in such a way as to provide benefit for this particular process but in doing so may preclude gaining the full benefits in other areas in the future. To obtain the full benefit, implementation decisions need to take into consideration all the uses to which the information will be put. Otherwise, it may mean a re-implementation of the system at a later date. This is not restricted to casemix systems. Dissatisfaction with a particular system, patient administration or nursing for example, so that it leads to the procurement of a replacement, is not unheard of. However, in many cases, it is not the system at fault but the way it was implemented. A re-implementation to meet current requirements may give the system an extended life. Of course, on occasion systems are wrongly procured and cannot do the job. Systems also do come naturally to the end of their useful life and need change.

The full implementation of a Casemix Management system can take from six months to more than two years. This depends on the available skills and resources, the sophistication of the system and the priority given to the different aspects of the system. It also depends on the current state and status of operational information systems within the hospital which will provide the source data. It is likely that a start will be made with inpatients and the information about them and their episodes of treatment as recorded on the patient administration system. Even this stage of implementation can start to be of immediate benefit for some auditing and monitoring of overall activity against expected. Some casemix analysis will be possible if coding of diagnoses and operative procedures is good and some linking to the contracting process is possible. It is a management decision as to how fast and how far the implementation goes from here.

All too often the implementation of Casemix Management systems is seen as a technical issue alone. All too often, once the technical installation is complete, data is routinely flowing into the system and tools to access the system are available and working, the project team is wound up and further implementation stops. It is the essential organisational implementation and development issues that are discussed in the remainder of this chapter since it is these rather than technical issues that normally limit the benefit that is obtained from management information.

Ownership

When an operational system is introduced, such as a Pathology system or Theatre system, the changed operational practices are defined, staff are trained in the new processes and, often, the ability to carry out the old practices is withdrawn. Staff need to use the technology in order to accomplish operational tasks. If all staff have been involved in the system selection, understand how it will help them and have been well trained in the use of the system, they will feel a sense of ownership. There will be greater benefit from the system than if staff had not been involved. Even without this sense of ownership, the system will be used and some benefits obtained.

Management information systems, such as the Casemix Management system, are very different and a sense of ownership is crucial to their success. The purpose of such systems is to support the management processes not to replace any operational processes. Benefits will be obtained from these systems only, if they are used and used appropriately. The sense of ownership will engender a desire to use the system and the information obtained from it. Good training will ensure that it is used easily and appropriately. Accurate, complete and relevant information will ensure continued use and satisfaction with the information obtained.

It is the concern of management that this ownership is engendered from the earliest possible stage. Ideally, this is started at the very early stages of the procurement process, with users being involved in discussions of their requirements and the importance that they attach to particular aspects of the system. Involvement of potential users at this stage will make all managers' lives easier.

Not everyone is going to be in this pleasant situation. What happens if users, and indeed key managers, feel a sense that a system, that they do not like and do not want, has been imposed upon them? Whether the system is good, bad or indifferent is really irrelevant at this stage. It is there, the investment has been made and the hospital might as well get the most it can from it. It is essential to find out how the system can be implemented in such a way that it can assist in the management processes and the individual users can see how to obtain the benefits from it. The identification and development of product champions can help to spread benefit throughout the hospital.

The computer system does not need to be located on the hospital site for this sense of ownership to be generated. It is often appropriate to let someone else manage the hardware itself, leaving the hospital to concern itself with how the system and its information is going to be used.

Linking information to management structures

The Casemix Management system has been defined in such a way that it is robust and flexible and can change easily as management structures and processes change. When installed, the system will provide a large repository of data. It may be delivered with a range of standard reports and enquiries and a good reporting facility whereby additional reports can be written and stored for regular and *ad hoc* use. Almost certainly there will be a great deal of additional implementation work required to provide the range of reports required and to structure them in a way that they reflect local management structures.

The data can be analysed and grouped in all manner of ways. For example, it can be grouped by consultant, specialty, clinical team, patient group. Data relevant to particular departments can be extracted and reported as well as summaries for the hospital as a whole. Reports need to be set up in such a way that groupings relate to the management structures of the particular hospital. They also need to be set up in such a way that they aid communication between particular management levels or units. When management levels or units interface, there will be information in a common format available to both. This helps to move discussions from 'Is the data correct?' to a more constructive dialogue[6] of 'What does it mean?'. In a similar manner, information for each individual user will be structured into a number of levels so that they can quickly view the information that is required. They can quickly drill down from summary information to information of increasing detail but decreasing scope. This concept of hierarchical structuring of information is shown in Figure 33.

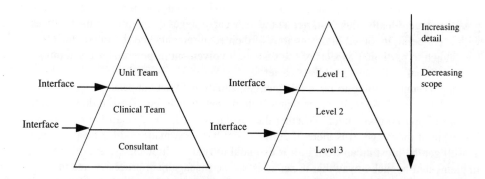

Figure 33. Hierarchical structuring

Figure 34 shows a clinical management structure typical of a Clinical Directorate model. In this example, each Directorate is managed by a team headed by a Director and supported by a Nurse Manager and a Business Manager. Service departments relate directly to the unit management team.

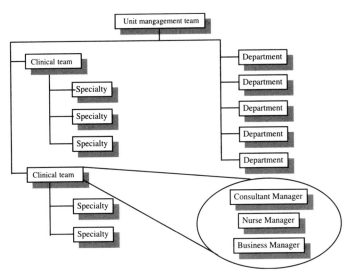

Figure 34. Clinical management structure

Two publications in particular discuss possible structures involving clinicians in the strategic and operational decision making of the hospital.[4,5] It needs to be recognised that the initial work will need to be continually revisited.

Whatever your own management structure, the information can be linked to it. Each role within the management structure will have a slightly different requirement for information. It is important that a consistency of routine reports is maintained throughout the organisation while providing the necessary scope and level of detail appropriate to individual responsibilities.

This is where the hard work of implementation begins. You may get some benefits from the reports that are supplied initially with the system but the real benefits are gained when the reports are tailored to link with the specific management structures and processes of a particular hospital and the data is turned into usable information.

Linking information to management processes

The hospital's particular objectives and the issues that it is currently addressing will determine the regular information required from the Casemix Management system. While reports delivered with the system will be of some benefit, it is important that the information available on a regular basis is tailored to the particular management processes of the individual hospital.

Some of these information needs will change infrequently. For example, having negotiated the contracts for a year, the way in which the information is used to monitor them is likely to remain the same until the contracts are re-negotiated. Particular issues that arise may need reports to be easily available, but over a more limited timescale.

A key element in being able to link information to management structures and processes is the patient groups that have been chosen for the definition of care profiles. In order to provide an integrated information environment, where expectations for budgets and contracts, for example, are based on clinical profiles, a single set of profiles used for monitoring purposes needs to be defined. These profiles can themselves be grouped in a number of different ways to reflect management structures, budgets and contracts. While grouped in different ways, the profiles are all based on clinically coherent groups. The items within the profiles will be defined by clinicians. Figure 35 shows profiles linked to management structures. Typically, the majority of the work within each specialty is covered by 20–30 profiles. Further discussion on linkages for this and other purposes can be found in Chapter 7, Care profiles.

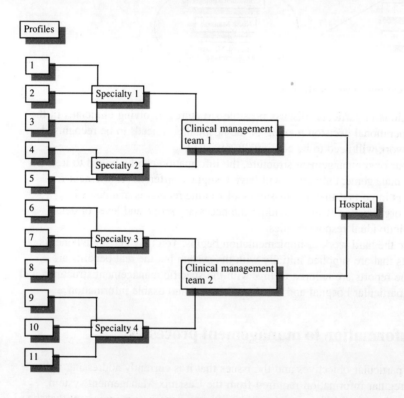

Figure 35. Profiles linked to management structures

You may, for example, have chosen to define profiles used for management purposes by Healthcare Resource Groups,[6] developed by the National Casemix Office. You may find that these groups cannot be amalgamated in such a way that they relate to structures and processes and, for example, that patients allocated to a single Healthcare Resource Group are treated by more than one clinical management team. In this situation you would need to sub-divide the group in order to allocate patients appropriately for local circumstances.

The evolutionary nature of information use

The management information that is required will constantly change. The objectives of individuals and the organisation as a whole will change, requiring alterations to the reporting. The issues to be tackled will change as a result of changing circumstances.

It must also be recognised that the experience of the users and the use of the information itself will contribute to a change in the requirements. There are four stages in the process (see Figure 36):

- Gaining confidence in the data and its accuracy.
- Converting the data to information, for example via simple descriptive statistics.
- Linking more complex information to management processes, e.g. variation analysis.
- Exception reporting: only reporting information when it is outside defined parameters.

In the early stages of use of a new system, or a new user of the information, or where information is being used to address a new issue, it is essential that simple reports are available to ensure that confidence is gained in the data and its accuracy.

When users know the data to be complete and accurate, they can then have confidence in using information generated from it to describe what is happening; levels of activity, cost and quality indicators. Understanding what is happening provides a basis for defining groups, profiles and expected numbers of cases: reflecting the estimates and plans for clinical activity and cost.

Information can then be linked to management processes with more complex reports showing how actual activity varies from that which was expected. To act on variations requires that the expectations defined by care profiles and expected numbers of cases are robust; otherwise variations may only be telling you that the plans were inappropriate.

In the final stage, it is unnecessary to report information comprehensively. Given confidence in the expectations that have been defined, it is appropriate for routine monitoring only to report that information that varies from what was expected or planned.

Even experienced users are likely to have requirements at the different stages. New users will need to progress through the stages.

This has implications for the information support that is provided to the users. To get the best out of any management information system, good professional information skills must be available to support users in their use of the system. They should provide such services as:

- Assistance in defining and satisfying information requirements.
- Advice on accuracy of the data.
- Advice on interpreting the information.

The tools provided with a Casemix Management system allow local tailoring of reports as the requirements of the change. Training in the use of the tools and in the support process is required.

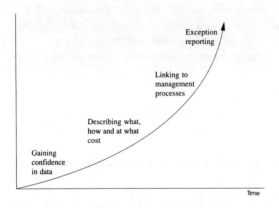

Figure 36. Evolutionary nature of use of information

Costs

The costs used within the Casemix Management system are standard costs of individual events. Each cost is split into a number of different elements such as fixed, variable, direct and indirect. In particular, this allows the linking of casemix information to budgets. Increasingly, budgets for elements of service department cost are forming part of clinical team budgets. Clinical teams can generally only control that element which is directly related to quantity, that is, the variable cost. Fixed costs may well be allocated to the individual service department. If casemix information is to be used as part of the budgetary process or for internal trading, then careful consideration needs to be given as to how these standard costs are calculated, how they are monitored against actual costs and how different elements are to relate to different budgets.

Casemix Management systems vary greatly in the costing facilities they provide over and above the minimum requirements. There are some which will allow the calculation of standard costs by a variety of means, have direct links to the general ledger system to monitor standard costs against actual costs and even contain full budgeting facilities.

Those systems that originated in the US are normally well developed in this area. Others merely record the costs that you input. Consequently the implementation issues vary greatly. Whichever system is in place, the following issues will need to be addressed:

- How and where are standard costs to be calculated?
- How are standard costs to be monitored against actual costs?
- How frequently and when will changes to standard costs be allowed?
- How are budgets going to be monitored?

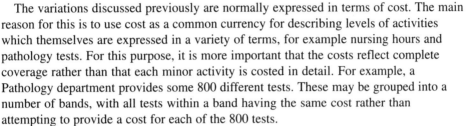

The variations discussed previously are normally expressed in terms of cost. The main reason for this is to use cost as a common currency for describing levels of activities which themselves are expressed in a variety of terms, for example nursing hours and pathology tests. For this purpose, it is more important that the costs reflect complete coverage rather than that each minor activity is costed in detail. For example, a Pathology department provides some 800 different tests. These may be grouped into a number of bands, with all tests within a band having the same cost rather than attempting to provide a cost for each of the 800 tests.

Since not all events will be captured in the early stages of an implementation, in order to get complete coverage some costs will be apportioned on the basis of an attendance, a patient day or patient group.

Costs are discussed further in Chapter 8.

Defining profiles

As previously described, profiles are the key to effective planning and monitoring. They describe the expected pattern of care and, when linked to the expected number of cases, provide the expectation of clinical activity and cost which allows the clinical process to be the basis for all management processes. Their structure and definition is therefore an essential implementation consideration.

The first decision to make when defining profiles is what patient groups the profiles should relate to. Not only should these be clinical and resource coherent groups but should also be capable of being grouped in such a way as to relate to the management structures and processes of the hospital. It is essential that clinicians are involved in all stages of selecting appropriate groups and profile definition.

The easiest way to start defining the profiles for each group is to collect actual data over a period of some 3-6 months. Analysis of this data into the same groups as the profiles will define what is actually happening to patients within these groups. But what is actually happening is not necessarily what is desirable. Discussions with clinicians will identify any desirable modifications including anticipated clinical changes. Such changes, for example in length of inpatient stay, shift from inpatient to day patient or change in Theatre time, for particular groups may have a considerable impact on the contracting processes.

This method is a lot easier and more productive that starting with a blank sheet of paper to try to define profiles.

A Casemix Management system will allow the definition of sets of profiles at a number of different levels for different purposes. To be able to link to all hospital budgets, contracts and management levels, these profiles in total should cover all the patients, with no gaps and no overlaps: each patient will be covered by one and only one profile in the set.

Care profiles are discussed further in Chapter 7.

When is casemix information usable?

It takes quite a long time to implement a Casemix Management system fully: somewhere between six months and two years depending on which operational systems the hospital has in place, the current status of organisational development and the level of cost accounting in practice.

One major incentive to increase the pace of implementation may be the rate at which the hospital becomes more specific in its contracts, moving from block to cost and volume contracts. With this, the need to be able to monitor activity and cost of a patient group or individual patient basis increases. Guidance from the NHS Management Executive on the use of HRGs as the basis for contracts makes the sort of information discussed in this book essential if the risk of contracting to the provider is to be reduced. Unexpected changes in mix of cases within a profile or the treatment pattern of particular groups of patients can have a major impact on costs associated with this type of contract.

Over a period of time, individual events from more departments will be included in the casemix system. Initially, it may be that only the major department events, such as Pathology, Radiology, Pharmacy, Operating Theatres and nursing hours are included, but this does not preclude linking the information to major management processes such as contracting and budgeting.

Completeness covers not only which events are included on the patient record but which areas of the hospital are involved in implementation. For example, implementation may be started as a pilot in a single clinical directorate.

The availability of event costing is important to link to budgeting and contracting. It is a management decision, of both general and clinical management, on the degree of detail of costing and the manner in which overheads are apportioned.

These aspects will be defined in the implementation plan and will determine the speed at which information becomes available to link to the key management processes of planning, monitoring, budgeting and contracting.

Given that the implementation issues are resolved, the information can be used almost immediately. The normal reporting period will be one month and as soon as one month's data is available then some use can be made of the system. A period of gaining confidence in the data and ensuring its accuracy is likely to be required. It will be some months before any trends can be identified. Use of the information to link to budgets or contracts can be commenced at any stage in the process, negotiation, setting, monitoring or review. Monitoring is most effectively carried out by starting at the period to which the contract or budget applies.

Security

Security of access to the information within a Casemix Management system is an important issue and needs to be considered at the implementation stage. Modern systems can restrict access to particular records or particular data items within records. For management purposes, there is no need to access individual patient records but only to access aggregated information. Such restrictions can be implemented.

The other aspect of security is, who can change what and when? This applies to expected numbers of cases, care profiles used for management purposes and event costs. These aspects reflect the plans of the hospital and as such can create havoc if not changed in a controlled manner. Library files also need to be kept up to date with any changes. Library files are lists of all those items that are coded on the patient record such as consultants, wards, diagnosis and operative procedures and many more.

Access can be restricted to particular users of the system. Who can change what and when will vary from hospital to hospital and the rules about this need to be decided at the time of implementation.

Changes to care profiles, costs and expected number of cases

Care profiles, costs and expected number of cases effectively form the plan of activity for the hospital and provide the link to budgeting and contracting processes. Who can change these variables and when it is important if casemix information is to be used effectively as part of management processes. Decisions need to be made as part of the implementation process. Plans will change throughout the year but it is important that these changes are controlled and that all those with a need to know of changes are informed of those changes. Uncontrolled change of any of these items will mean that the Casemix Management system cannot provide the powerful information that it is capable of delivering.

Information support function

The information support function within the hospital is critical to the success of Casemix Management and other management information systems. Many Information departments see themselves as providing a high quality centralised service whereby they produce the information for the users on request. This has developed from the time when computer-based information was difficult to extract and could only be provided in the form of printed reports. The tools used were complex to use and great skill was required if the information obtained was not to be inaccurate or misleading. It was very easy to think you had asked one question of the system to receive a response to something completely different. Until recently, a response period of 24 hours was common before the required information could be obtained.

With the current generation of systems, this type and level of response is no longer adequate or necessary. Much of the information required can be displayed on a screen and can be available as and when the user requires it. The problem of thinking one question is being asked when, in fact, it is another that is being asked, still exists. This is where a good, well trained and supportive information service is essential. Skilled information staff are required to set up routine views and reports for the users and ensure that these are maintained as requirements change. They will also need to provide a resource for *ad hoc* reporting as required.

Some Information departments see greater user involvement in obtaining and using information as a threat to their position. On the contrary, organisational development needs to address this issue in such a way that, while the role is changed, the status within the organisation is maintained or indeed strengthened as the problem of interpreting data from many sources becomes more complex.

Implementation checklist

- A sense of ownership in users is essential.
  - ◊ Involve users at all stages.
  - ◊ Listen to users at every opportunity; they are generally right.
- Identify and develop product champions.
- Link information to management structures.
  - ◊ Determine scope and level of detail of information for individual roles.
  - ◊ Provide common information where managers interface.
  - ◊ Provide consistent information throughout the organisation.
- Structure reports to give information of decreasing scope and increasing detail.
- Link information to management processes.
  - ◊ The key to linkage is in the definition of care profiles.
  - ◊ A single set of profiles is defined to map to structures and processes.
  - ◊ Profiles are defined for clinically coherent groups and mapped to processes.
  - ◊ Profile items are defined by clinicians.
- Recognise stages of information use.
  - ◊ Gaining confidence in the data and its accuracy.
  - ◊ Converting the data to information, for example via simple descriptive statistics.
  - ◊ Linking more complex information to management processes, e.g. variation analysis.
  - ◊ Exception reporting; only reporting information when it is outside defined parameters.

- Costs.
  - ◊ How and where are standard costs to be calculated?
  - ◊ How are standard costs to be monitored against actual costs?
  - ◊ How frequently and when will changes to standard costs be allowed?
  - ◊ How are budgets going to be monitored?
  - ◊ Ensure complete coverage.
- Defining profiles.
  - ◊ Involve clinicians throughout.
  - ◊ Select patient groups which can map to structures and processes.
  - ◊ Base profiles on the actual process of care.
  - ◊ For the management profile set, ensure each patient is included in one and only one profile.
- Security.
  - ◊ Determine who can change what and when: management profile set, costs, expected numbers of cases associated with management profiles.
  - ◊ Ensure security of access.
- Ensure provision of skilled information support.

5. Describing patients and processes

Patient identification

Most hospitals are not in the fortunate position of having an integrated, patient-based operational system which provides a single patient master index and single patient identifier. In many cases several patient identification numbers will be used by different departments. Details of the patients will normally come from a patient administration system. Events such as pathology tests, nursing hours, etc., are obtained from departmental operational systems. These events are linked to a particular patient primarily through the patient identification number. It is not surprising therefore that, where several patient numbering systems are used, there are a number of errors in attempting to attach events to patients within the management information system. These are time consuming to resolve.

As part of the national Information Management and Technology Strategy, the NHS Executive decided that the NHS number should be established as the unique patient identifier throughout health systems.[7] Since the current number is not appropriate for use in modern information systems, the executive initiated a project to replace the current number with one that could be used. This will ensure easier linkage of events but could not be justified on provision of internal management information alone. It will also facilitate the transfer of personal information while maintaining the high degree of privacy that is required. It is also intended to facilitate the exchange of information between clinicians and between organisations, for example the transfer of maternity records from hospital to the community.

Coding diagnoses and operative procedures

The rationale behind the Casemix Management system is that patients can be grouped for analysis by any combination of data items on the record. However, the main grouping on which other groups linking to management processes are based is a grouping which exhibits clinical and resource coherence. The Diagnosis Related Group (DRG) is one such example. Both the DRG and other measures such as the Healthcare Resource Groups (HRGs) defined by the National Casemix Office of the NHS Executive rely on accurate and complete coding of diagnoses and operative procedures. Clinicians also recognise the importance of this for audit purposes.

As part of the Resource Management programme most hospitals took
to raise the profile of coding, train the coders and move their activity mu<
clinical process. The use of clinically coded data as part of the contracting
provided a remarkable incentive to further improvements; the income of the
now depended on the complete clinical coding of patient records. Investmen<
coders is a key part of this process and there are now training courses and con
based training packages that can help.[8] While the Resource Management progr
organised national and more local initiatives to improve coding, and provided a<
impetus within many hospitals to start their own programmes, the accurate and
complete coding of diagnosis and operative procedures for clinical and audit purposes
remains equally important.

A variety of coding systems are used within England but all of them can map back to
a common standard; for diagnostic coding this is ICD9 (International Classification of
Diseases, 9th revision)[9] and OPCS4[10] (Office of Population Censuses and Surveys
operative procedures coding, 4th revision). Others used are ICD9-CM,[11] a clinical
modification of ICD9 to allow more detailed coding of diagnoses, and increasingly, the
READ codes.[12] Devised by Dr James Read, these are now developed and maintained by
the National Centre for Coding and Classification of the NHS Executive.

The READ codes form the basis of 'The Clinical Thesaurus of Terms', which has
been agreed by the medical profession and is supported by the NHS Executive. They
form a key part of the national Information Management and Technology Strategy.[13] The
development of READ codes started in the early 1980s and originated in Primary Care.
In 1990 they were endorsed by the medical profession as the standard clinical coding
system in General Practice. They have since received extensive support for use in
hospitals.

READ codes provide a hierarchically arranged thesaurus of terms used in health care.
By the end of 1992, over 100,000 preferred terms were included with a synonym list of
150,000. These codes are mapped to most widely used standard classification systems
including ICD9, ICD9CM, OPCS4, RCGP 1986,[14] ICPC and Oxmis.[15] There are also
mappings to other classifications such as the British National Formulary and the WHO
ATC classification.[16] The mappings enable the data captured as READ codes to be
analysed according to these other systems.

There are also several computer programs that can be used to help the coding process
itself. These help coders to code more accurately and quickly. Whatever coding system
you are using, ICD9, ICD9-CM or Read codes, there is a product that can help. These
products are described in a booklet published by the Resource Management Unit 'Survey
of Encoders' which is included in a Coding Pack.[17] There are, in essence, two types of
products: those that merely look up a code from text that is keyed in by the user and
those that include some intelligence, guiding the user to a full and valid coding of the
patient record. The different level of benefit available from the two types and the
required complexity of the product are reflected in the price.

Grouping patients

The importance of being able to group patients in clinical and resource coherent groups crops up time and time again. Such a means of grouping is crucial to the Casemix Management system if the information is to be used for supporting management processes such as planning, monitoring, budgeting and contracting. They form the basis for the definition of care profiles defining the expected process of care for groups of patients.

Diagnosis Related Groups (DRGs) were developed in the US for this purpose and later used for the prospective payments system. There is now considerable experience of the use of DRGs in England which is documented in a number of publications.[18,19,20] This started with a study in 1982 when researchers at the London School of Hygiene carried out an evaluation of DRGs on a national sample of inpatient episode data. The study took two years to complete and identified potential for DRGs to be used for service planning and monitoring. Another study at this time was by CASPE which examined the way in which casemix might vary if consultants were given control of their own budgets. The results did not show any evidence of casemix changes but there was some evidence of reduced resource use when compared to control sites.

Work on casemix groupings was given further impetus with the launch of the Resource Management initiative in 1986 which ultimately saw the introduction of Casemix Management systems into all large acute hospitals.

A number of difficulties were identified in using DRGs in the UK. Some of the DRGs are not clinically coherent in the US either; in some cases very different cases are included in the same group because overall resource usage is similar. Some do not work in the UK because practice differs from that in the US; for example, in the United Kingdom endoscopies are usually performed as day cases whereas in the US they are not. For these and other reasons, the National Casemix Office of the NHS Executive undertook work on devising an English grouping known as Healthcare Resource Groups (HRGs). The work was led by Dr Hugh Sanderson who had submitted the proposal for an initial study into DRGs back in 1981. This development had significant clinical input and work is proceeding on analysis of these inpatient groups to determine their resource coherence.

HRGs were primarily developed to manage resources and set contract prices. To do this they must allow prediction of the expected use of resources for patients within each group.

There are a number of other grouping algorithms devised for other types of patients, such as:

- Ambulatory Visit Groups (AVGs) for outpatients.[21]
- Ambulatory Patient Groups (APGs) for outpatients.
- Resource Utilisation Groups (RUGs) for long-stay patients.

A useful introduction to grouping is provided in a computer-based training package 'Grouping Patients for Doctors and Managers'.[22]

Table 14 gives some key dates for grouping of patient records.

1914	Early attempts to define the product of a hospital. Codman E.A.[23]
1960s	Initial work on measuring and costing output of hospitals. Fetter.
1965	Feldstein advocates use of standard patient groups for comparing efficiency of hospitals.[24]
1973	Documentation of patient groups by Yale University.
1975	Definition and development of European MBDS accepted as top priority by Commission of European Communities (CEC DGXIII)
1981	London School of Hygiene submits proposal to Chief Scientist for evaluation of DRGs using national data sample.
1982	European MBDS officially recommended by CEC as basis for management planning and evaluation of health services.
1983	DRGs adopted in US for prospective payments - Medicare. First national DRG version used by HCFA (470 groups)
1984	First annual workshop of Patient Classification Systems - Europe (PCS/E). Co-ordinated network to encourage exchange of ideas. Paris.
1986	Experimental use of DRGs in UK as part of Resource Management programme commenced.
1990	Portugal bases system of resource distribution among hospitals on DRGs.
1991	Norway commences implementation of patient groups. Partial DRG-based reimbursement for inpatient care.
1991	Development of reference model to allow comparison of patient-based data across Europe (AIM project HOSCOM).
1992	Introduction of AP-DRGs version 9 in US (619 groups).
1992	Development of HRGs in UK.
1993	Investigation of use of HRGs as basis for contract categories in UK.

Table 14. Key dates for grouping patient records

The Casemix Management system will allow grouping of patient records by a variety of means and it is to be expected that different grouping algorithms will be used for different purposes.

Contract categories

The National Casemix Office used HRGs as the basis for the development of contract categories based on the development of HRGs. The first version of these was published in April 1993.[25] These categories covered hospital inpatients in the 16 highest volume specialties and were based on the analysis of data from ten English regions (approximately 6.3 million consultant episodes). The HRGs accounting for either 70 per cent or 80 per cent of the bed–days for each specialty form separate categories. The remaining HRGs for each specialty are grouped into either three or four bands on the basis of geometric mean length of stay.

Table 15 shows how cardiology patients were grouped into categories using the 70 per cent and three band limits.

Quality measures

It is vital that consideration of the quality of care is seen as an integral part of the general management processes of the hospital. It is not simply the responsibility of the audit processes undertaken by clinical staff, but a corporate responsibility. Quality issues will increasingly be raised as part of the contracting process and subject to contractual agreements. There is also growing evidence, mainly from the US, that high quality care is also cost-effective care.[26] It is no coincidence that commercial companies throughout

HRG	Description	% bed days
E14	Circulatory Disorders with AMI w/o CV Comp Disch Alive	11.0
E18	Heart failure/shock	9.3
E04	Heart & Main Vessels - Category 3	7.5
E07	Perm Cardiac Pacemaker Implant w/o AMI, Heart Failure or Shock	7.0
E11	Circulatory Disorders (exc AMI w Card Cath w/o Complex Diag)	6.2
E19	Angina Pectoris	5.8
E17	Cardiac Arrhythmia & Conduction Disorders w/o cc	4.6
E02	Heart & Main Vessels - Category 5	4.4
E21	Atherosclerosis w/o cc	3.7
E01	Heart & Main Vessels - Category 7	3.7
E29	Chest Pain	3.4
E23	Cardiac Congenital & Valvular Disorders w/o cc	2.8
	Band 1	11.0
	Band 2	12.6
	Band 3	5.5

Table 15. Cardiology contract categories

the world have enthusiastically adopted quality programmes; quality affects the bottom line. Health care is no different in wanting to provide high quality with increasing emphasis being put not only on quality as defined by health care professionals but also on the views of patients.

One organisation that has adopted the concept of Total Quality Management is Intermountain Health Care in Salt Lake City, Utah. Quality is now very much a part of the culture of the organisation. It gives four main reasons why it adopted the concept:[27]

- Quality focuses on the core business, clinical medicine.
- Quality/process improvement is sound business strategy.
- Quality controls cost and it is marketable to buyers of the core business.
- Quality truly adds *value* to our customers.

It identified nine principles of quality improvement:

- Quality controls cost.
- Health care is a system.
- 'Good enough' is NOT good enough.
- Match management to variation.
- Quality management is NOT a matter of opinion.
- Caring balances curing.
- It takes a team.
- Our business is clinical medicine.
- A quality organisation is not something you buy; it's something you grow.

In the following section we consider how each of these principles might be interpreted in the light of the UK situation.

1. Quality controls cost

There are a number of areas where poor quality increases costs:

- Unnecessary interventions; for example diagnostic tests, medications.
- 'Getting it right first time'; for example the cost of revisions of hip replacements and unsuccessful keyhole surgery.
- Avoidable complications; for example post-operative infections.
- Imbalance of resources; for example lack of Theatre time or access to diagnostic facilities leading to increased length of stay.
- Employee turnover and consequent training costs.

There are a number of factors driving overall costs up which are putting increasing pressure on the health care system which cannot be controlled; the increasing elderly population, epidemiological disease and the possibilities offered by new technology. This gives even more reason for reducing individual patient costs wherever possible.

Since standard cost of events are used as the basis of costing within a Casemix Management system, increased cost is a direct reflection of increased activity. Cost can

therefore be used as an overall measure of the treatment process and therefore as a broad measure of quality of the process.

2. Health care is a system

The complete process of health care is made up of a number of subcomponents. The optimisation of one of these components does not necessarily optimise the whole process. For example, some early discharge schemes may result in a greater number of readmissions or extensive care in the community while the quality and cost of the original inpatient episode, seen in isolation, may be improved. Unless the whole process is investigated, an apparent increase in quality in one area may not be reflected in the whole.

To measure the quality of the entire process of care requires that the discrete episodes making that care can be linked and expectations set for that complete period of care. This is beyond the scope of most existing management information systems. With the increasing implementation of integrated patient-based operational systems in hospitals (HISS systems) and the development of the electronic medical record, it becomes feasible to consider such systems for the future. A research project is considering the model on which such systems of the future will be based.

3. 'Good enough' is NOT good enough!

This particularly puts the focus on the process of eliminating unacceptable practice which is the approach of traditional quality assurance methods. Elimination of practice which is outside a certain target or standard does not imply that the rest is in any way excellent. The aim should be improvement in the process for everyone.

Improvements are measured by shifts in distributions rather than just the elimination of exceptional cases.

4. Match management to variation

This assumes that there is an element of variation in the health care process that is not random, following the laws of probability. There are elements of variation that can be traced, identified and managed, hence improving the process.

In defining coherent groups and setting expectations for the process of care, existing systems are very much based on this concept. That variation due to a volume, process and casemix can be identified and appropriate actions required to influence each taken. An understanding of the stability of the process with attempts made to stabilise unstable processes is essential.

5. Quality management is NOT a matter of opinion

Continuous quality improvements are made through identifying key influencing factors on the process, measuring and continuously monitoring these factors. Feedback is as important to quality management as to any other area.

58

It is as important to measure patient satisfaction and make those directly involved in the process aware of the results as it is to measure outcomes and process. Casemix Management information is an essential element in this measurement and continuous monitoring.

6. Caring balances curing

Patient satisfaction is increasingly taken to be as important a measure of quality as outcome. It needs to be managed as does process and outcome.

7. It takes a team

Most work is done in teams. To improve quality, we need to ensure that the knowledge of all is shared if major improvements in quality are to be made and sustained. Often quality is only as good as the weakest link. Everyone in the team needs to understand that improving how they do their job is part of the job. Management needs to ensure that appropriate infrastructure and training are available.

8. Our business is clinical medicine

Business processes must be firmly based on clinical activity. There need not be a conflict, as is so often the case, if the business processes are designed to sustain and develop the clinical activities with quality being central to the business. This does not mean that funds are not limited or that difficult choices need not be made. Difficult choices must be made particularly when the quality of health care for groups of patients or a larger population come into conflict with quality of care for an individual, particularly where that individual care is 'high tech', extremely expensive and likely to be of limited success.

9. A quality organisation is not something you buy; it's something you grow

Continuous quality improvement is just what the name implies. It requires a change in attitude throughout the organisation. It must start with enthusiastic clinicians, given support and involvement from the top of the organisation, and build on success. This chapter has focused on the need and means of measuring quality. However, if there is not the willingness by everyone in the organisation to improve quality, the ability to measure it is of no use.

Casemix information is fundamental to the measurement of the quality of the care process and of outcomes. Care profiles define the expected process or the events that a group of similar patients would be expected to have during their period of treatment and care. These can then be used to monitor what actually happens. Provision of more, less or different care than is appropriate for a particular patient is an indication that quality can be improved and is a matter for consideration by audit.

Since process also determines the cost of clinical care, there are significant implications for management. Process issues may also form part of the contract with purchasers.

Outcome measures of quality are another important issue. When appropriate outcome measures are defined, these can also be incorporated into the Casemix Management system, monitored and used in the contract negotiations. However, for some patients the outcome on discharge may be uncertain and procedures for follow-up over several months or years may be necessary. This is further complicated by the fact that the expected or possible outcome may vary for different patients within a patient group. The clinical and resource coherent groups appropriate for other aspects may not prove to be coherent for outcome.

Number of adverse events forms yet another measure of quality. Common examples are the prevalence of nosocomial infections, post-operative returns to surgery or the mortality rate for a particular group of patients. Expected data for such events can be included on the profiles and actual rates compared with them.

Patient satisfaction is a critical factor in determining the quality of care and which, at present, is normally measured by carrying out surveys. Patient satisfaction information should be brought together with objective measures of clinical quality. The results of detailed questionnaires from individual patients is not appropriate data to input to a Casemix Management system. However, an indicator generated from such questionnaires would be.

Coding investigations and other events

There is no standard method of coding investigations such as Pathology Tests, Radiology, etc., which is used throughout the UK. Often the coding method is specific to a particular operational system or is determined by an individual site at the implementation of a system. This provides difficulties where comparisons across different hospitals or transfer of data are required.

The National Centre for Coding and Classification supports the Professions Allied to Medicine and Nursing Terms Projects which are identifying and coding terms used by chiropodists, physiotherapists, speech therapists, dieticians, occupational therapists and nursing.

Grouping investigations and other events

The level of coding required at the clinical level is far more detailed than that required for management purposes. This applies as much to investigations and other events as it does to diagnoses and operative procedures.

For example, at the clinical level, Pathology generates some 800 codes. There is no common agreed standard for grouping of events. While clinical level coding can be used for management purposes, it is desirable that a means of grouping events is devised.

There are no standard groupings recognised for other events but some information systems use locally derived grouping, particularly for the purpose of monitoring the use of resources. In particular, for management purposes, it is unnecessary to define profiles at the level of individual diagnostic test although the patient level information may be recorded at this level of detail.

Obtaining data from operational systems

The Casemix Management system is a management information system. It does not need data to be immediately up to date; updating once a week is probably sufficient although most systems will update at least every day. The users will often be carrying out complex analyses of the data. This is very different from an operational system, for example patient administration, where users will normally be looking at a single record and changing the information in it. The two types of system have very different requirements and therefore, with few exceptions, perform more effectively in separate computer environments. This raises the problem of how the data on patients and events gets into the Casemix Management system.

Unless an integrated hospital information system or an order communications and results reporting system is installed, the data will normally be transferred from a variety of operational department systems, such as Patient Administration, Pathology etc. At the implementation stage, links with these various systems need to be established, which can be quite a costly process. Incompatibilities between the way in which data is coded on the different systems can become an issue. There is a requirement for the Casemix Management system to validate the incoming data to ensure its compatibility. There is also an issue of timing the transfer of data from different systems to ensure that there is a patient record to attach individual events to. Even so, hospitals have demonstrated that this form of data capture is effective given that data is obtained from the Patient Administration system and a minimum of two from Pathology, Radiology, Pharmacy and Operating Theatres.

It is certainly easier to obtain the data from an integrated system or an order communications and results reporting system. There is a single link to the Casemix Management system making communications between systems cheaper and less prone to failure. Data is validated in the operational systems, where any errors identified can be corrected by those who have an operational use for that data and an immediate interest in its accuracy.

It is not feasible or desirable to key data directly into the Casemix Management system other than for departments where the volume is too small to warrant the introduction of some form of operational computer system of their own or access to order communications or results reporting. With the current capabilities and price of microcomputers this is unlikely to be the case. The only way to obtain accurate and relevant data for the management information system is to transfer it from the operational systems. If the data is no use to the operational department, then it is absolutely no use to management either.

Dates of events

While the various events that take place during the clinical process are obtained from individual department systems, they will be linked to a particular patient episode within the Casemix Management system itself.

Individual events are linked to the patient episode through the date of event and the start and end dates of the episode. There may be requests dated before the beginning of an episode which are relevant to that episode, for example, pre-admission requests. There may also be tests carried out after the formal completion of the episode.

This requires a sophisticated matching system; otherwise the automatic linkage fails. Records that are rejected because they cannot be linked must then be manually reconciled to the correct records. If this happens in a large number of cases, the process can be extremely time consuming.

6. Patient-based management information systems

Casemix in England

The concept of patient-based management information systems, and Casemix management in particular, was given a major boost as part of the Resource Management programme launched in 1986. The programme was principally one of the organisational development of acute hospitals, encouraging the devolution of management: 'Doctors in Management'. An essential element of the programme was to ensure that this organisational development was underpinned by a patient-based information system.

The objectives of the programme were formally set out in HN(86)34.[28] The incorporation of additional local objectives into the programme, set by the hospitals themselves, was encouraged. The principal objective was:

- The introduction of a new approach to resource management and to demonstrate whether or not this resulted in measurable improvements in patient care,

with subsidiary objectives to:

- Identify areas of waste and inefficiency.
- Benefit from clinical group discussion and review.
- Highlight areas which could most benefit from more resources.
- Identify and expose the health care consequences of given financial policies and constraints.
- Understand the comparative costs of future health care options and hold informed debates about such options.

Those hospitals in the lead in this area contracted external companies to define the requirements of the information systems and determine whether there were appropriate systems in existence which could be procured to meet the requirements. Systems in use in the US were investigated but the conclusion at the time was that there were no systems appropriate to meet the objectives of the Resource Management programme. Since that time a number of systems originating in the US have provided satisfactory results, given some modification.

Three companies embarked on the development of systems to meet the system's requirements of the pilot sites:

- KPMG Peat, Marwick, McLintock with Huddersfield Royal Infirmary.
- ISTEL (now AT&T ISTEL) with Freeman Hospital, Newcastle, and Royal Hampshire County Hospital, Winchester.
- ICL with Pilgrim Hospital, Boston, Lincolnshire.

The other two pilot sites, Guy's Hospital, London, and Arrowe Park Hospital, Wirral, procured the AT&T ISTEL and KPMG systems, respectively.

In September 1988, the central Resource Management Unit undertook a review of the requirements to support the Resource Management process. This review covered three main areas:

- Systems being developed in the pilot hospitals.
- Systems implemented in other countries, primarily the US.
- A bottom-up requirements definition from the objectives of the programme.

It was found that none of the systems being developed in the pilot hospitals could fully meet the objectives of the programme at that time although, between them, they had all the necessary elements. All of these systems have now been developed so they meet the minimum requirements and more. It was also found that some of the systems in the US very nearly met the minimum requirements and with minimal modifications may well transfer to the UK. Most of the systems, however, would require major modification.

The review resulted in the publication of the 'Casemix Management System Core Specification' by the central Resource Management Unit, which describes the elements of a system that are necessary to support the objectives of the Resource Management Initiative.[2]

By 1993, some 12 commercial systems were available that met the minimum requirements, and the majority of acute hospitals had procured Casemix Management systems.

Experience in the US

Patient-based systems giving details of the patients themselves and their events were introduced in hospitals in the US and were originally implemented for the purposes of billing. In 1983, the United States Congress passed the Social Security Amendments which established the Prospective Payment System (PPS) for Medicare inpatient hospital services (Public Law 98-21). This necessitated the introduction of patient-based information systems where patient records were completely and accurately coded for diagnoses and operative procedures and could be grouped into Diagnosis Related Groups (DRGs) to ensure payment.

DRGs developed from work undertaken by Robert B. Fetter and his team, which was looking for a way to measure the cost and cost the output of a hospital in the 1960s.

Developments continued through the 1970s.

The original intention of the casemix grouping was to provide a tool for the clinical and administrative management of hospitals and to help maintain the quality of care while minimising the cost of that care; not dissimilar to the English requirement for a system.

Many of the US systems focused more on the cost side than the quality. For example, most systems originating in the US contain DRG optimisation programmes although this feature is not normally accessible in UK implementations. This is a computer program which rearranges the order of diagnoses in order to ensure maximum reimbursement for the case. It should be said that some of the systems did take quality seriously and these are the ones that have more successfully been implemented here.

Most attention in the development of US systems focused on inpatients, and this has also been the case in England. There were a number of reasons for this. The prospective payments systems at the time related only to inpatients and inpatients generate the majority of a hospital's cost. Inpatient systems are easier to develop and implement since the required data has been collected for a long time in manual records. The DRG as a measure of casemix had been developed some time before and was tried and tested. On the outpatient side, records were not routinely coded and there was no such established casemix measure. Collection of data from outpatients raises many difficulties which have not yet been resolved. For example, a number of episodes of care may run concurrently and extend over several years, there is not always a diagnosis by which to describe the patient and grouping algorithms for outpatients have not been tested.

Because of the time when Casemix Management systems were originally developed in the US, when technology did not offer the opportunities for simple access that it does today, and also the association with prospective payments, there are normally two areas where a typical US system will not meet UK requirements unless it has been modified. Care profiles were an element of the system missing from many US systems. The reporting facilities for clinicians and managers to obtain rapid access to the information they require are frequently somewhat unsophisticated. Many of the systems were developed at a time when the information and possibly finance departments alone had direct access to the management information systems of the hospital.

That there is now knowledge and use of DRGs throughout the world stands testament to the years of work undertaken by Professor Fetter and his team, their commitment to open standards and their willing distribution of definitions and grouping methodology.

Views in other European countries

Although the methods of funding health services across different European countries vary tremendously, most countries are tackling the same problems and finding that the information systems required to help solve these problems are remarkably similar.

Most countries are facing increasing costs of health care and seeking ways of providing the best possible care for patients within the financing that is available. In many countries this is leading to devolved management structures and processes supported by patient-based information systems.

Most European countries have experimented with the use of DRGs and grouping methods are gradually being adopted for widespread use. In 1990, Portugal started to base the resource distribution between hospitals on the basis of DRGs.[29] In 1991, Norway embarked on the implementation of patient groups for the partial reimbursement of inpatient care.[30]

The EC funded the Advanced Informatics in Medicine (AIM) programme and the current TELEMATICS programme to promote the co-operation of European countries in the development of information systems to meet the requirements of health care. In particular the Hospital Comparisons in Europe project (HOSCOM) looked at the minimum data requirements for managing hospital resources.[31] The RICHE project looked at a common architecture for operational and management information systems in hospitals. The aim of the RICHE project is to construct a framework for overall information and communication systems for health care in Europe, and to demonstrate the feasibility of this approach.

In August 1991 the RICHE project management team published their overall framework,[32] which is summarised in Figure 37. This envisages future hospital systems that are based on the patient's medical and nursing records. Their emphasis is on the integration of direct medical and nursing information. They will contribute substantially to the quality of patient care and provide management information as a by-product of operational processes. Casemix management is just one of the elements of a future management information system.

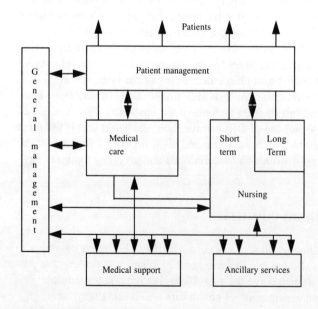

Figure 37. RICHE framework

There is extensive experience throughout Europe of the use of casemix measures, particularly the DRG. Various uses are described in 'Diagnosis Related Groups in Europe: Uses and Perspectives'.[33] Such uses include:

- Comparing use of hospital resources across a number of European countries.
- Outcomes management.
- Costing patient treatment.
- Funding hospitals.

The core system

The minimum requirements for a patient-based information system to support the objectives of the resource management programme was described in the NHS Management Executive document 'Casemix Management System Core Specification'.[2] This describes a management information system which is simple and can meet the changing requirements of management without great change in the system. This document was published just before the White Paper *Working for Patients* outlining the most fundamental changes in NHS management processes since 1948. On subsequent review of the core specification, a few data items needed to be added to link to the new contracting process. Otherwise the fundamental nature of the system remained unchanged.

The core system is the minimum required to meet the requirements of resource management. Most systems will contain many more data items than the minimum and many will also support other management processes such as costing, audit and contract monitoring in total. These additional functions may be required in the hospital's Casemix Management system, provided as separate systems or as part of other systems. The minimum data items are listed in Appendix C including changes following the White Paper and including other patient types.

The system combines data on activity and resource use from a variety of sources into a patient record. This allows all managers to have a co-ordinated view of how resources are being used and what benefits are being obtained from use of those resources in terms of individual patients and patient groups.

There are four main elements to the Casemix Management system:

- The individual patient records, including demographic details, diagnosis and operative procedures, and individual events such as Pathology tests, Radiology, Pharmacy, nursing hours, etc. These records can be grouped in a variety of ways such as casemix groups, consultants, specialties, clinical teams, etc.
- Care profiles which define the expected events for a particular group of patients.
- Multi-element standard costs at the level of an individual event. A cost of each event, for example a full blood count or an X-ray, which is split into a number of different elements, such as fixed, variable, direct, indirect, staff, non-staff, allows linkage of appropriate costs to the appropriate budget holders, groups or contracts.

67

• A high quality graphical reporting system that can provide information linked to the management processes and structures and provide for individual requirements. The system should be easily accessible and understood by the users and provide for *ad hoc* requirements as well as standard reporting.

The core specification relates only to inpatients although there is a clear indication that this should extend to cover all patients treated or cared for by the hospital. Most systems now do this.

Extending range of patients

While most hospitals start by collecting information on inpatients, it is equally important, both for improving patient care and improving the management of resources that information is available on all patients.

The distinction of patients as inpatients, outpatients, day patients, ward attenders, etc., has always been an administrative convenience. It has always caused some difficulty since not all patients fit neatly within the necessary definitions of different types of patient. Day patients had to occupy a bed. Outpatients were treated in outpatient departments. The fact that some patients would most appropriately be treated on a ward but would not occupy a bed led to the new definition of ward attender. With modern systems, we can now view the patient as a patient who has certain events (such as Pathology tests) in certain places (such as a ward). We can now view patients over their whole period of care, or patients who attend an outpatient clinic, or patients who attend a ward but do not occupy a bed. This may, at first, seem a trivial difference but has implications for information systems of the future and their ability to view quality and resource use issues across the entire period of care of a patient with a particular problem. Labels such as 'ward attender' can be attached later for aggregate statistical returns, if necessary.

Extending casemix systems to cover outpatients and accident and emergency patients is not as simple as it might at first seem. A number of sites and suppliers are working on this. The NHS Executive is supporting a number of projects in English hospitals to consider the following issues:

• How and when to classify outpatient records.
• How to allocate events to outpatient records when there may be more than one concurrent episode.
• How to define and when to view an outpatient episode when it might extend over several years.
• How to link outpatient events to related inpatient events in order to investigate total resource use and alternative methods of treatment.

Viewing the patient as the prime focus of attention will be the key to resolving many of these issues.

A study undertaken for the Department of Health in 1990[34] proposed a classification scheme for all patients where care is in an ambulatory setting; outpatients, A&E attendance's, ward attenders and day cases. The purpose of the classification system was primarily to support:

- Accounting for services.
- Pricing contracts.
- Resource management.

This proposed classification involved the definition of 'care stages' and the recording of a limited list of significant procedures during that care stage. The four care stages were described by the purpose of attendance as:

- Assessment.
- Treatment.
- Follow-up.
- Monitoring.

It was suggested that significant procedures would include diagnostic procedures associated with assessment attendances or therapeutic procedures associated with treatment attendances.

Medical audit

The information system's requirements to support medical and clinical audit are very similar to those required to support general management processes and are sensibly combined in a single system solution, at least in the longer term. All data required for supporting general management processes is also required for clinical management processes, and the technical requirements for access and performance are similar.

Many hospitals have purchased microcomputer systems, running a variety of different software for different specialties, to support the audit process. In addition to support of an audit programme, these systems often provide some operational support. For example, the system may include the production of standard discharge letters to GPs or support to the clinical coding process. Some even include facilities to schedule outpatients, which are more appropriately provided by a hospital-wide system.

There are a number of disadvantages of using separate medical audit microcomputer systems which the incorporation into the casemix environment can overcome. Most of the audit systems require that data is keyed directly in to them whereas casemix will obtain data from direct links to a range of operational systems such as Patient Administration, Pathology, Radiology, Pharmacy and Operating Theatres or, increasingly, from an order communications system. Manual input reduces accuracy and takes time. While some systems will take data directly from operational systems, the cost of providing multiple links between numerous systems is costly and difficult to manage. Many of the Casemix Management systems meet the requirements to support medical audit.

There are basically three options:

- Retain the separate audit systems and the inherent data problems.
- Link audit systems to a hospital-wide network in order to take advantage of data capture from operational systems and control a core set of data which is shared between all systems.
- Have a single system which meets the requirements of both resource management and audit.

Audit does add some additional requirements to the core requirements of the Casemix Management system.

- Additional data items are required, many of which are specific to a single specialty. For example, birth weight of newborn babies.
- Event details need to be more detailed than required for management purposes.
- Detailed data will be required for *ad hoc* surveys.

Many Casemix Management systems allow users to define their own information in addition to that which provides the core of the system which is able to meet these additional requirements.

Hospital information infrastructure

Casemix Management systems basically consist of a large repository of data along with some excellent analysis and presentation tools. They derive their data from the operational systems of the hospital. This is particularly important since this is the only way in which to ensure that the data within the management information system is accurate and complete. If the data is no use to the originating department, then it is certainly no use to management.

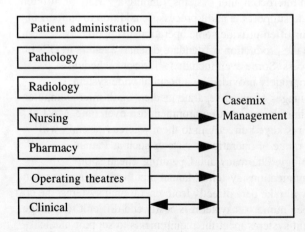

Figure 38. System configuration: early stage

Initially, data may be obtained from a variety of individual departmental systems with much of the linking of data items to form patient records being carried out in the casemix system itself. It can be costly and time consuming developing these links to provide good, timely data to casemix.

Where a hospital has an order communications and results reporting system, this is the most effective source of event data for casemix. However, in most hospitals data will be obtained from a variety of different operational systems. Figures 38 and 39 show typical configurations; one has an order communications system (Fig 39), the other not (Fig 38).

In this first configuration, difficulties often arise in linking event data from one system to patient data from another. This can lead to a reduction in data accuracy and the need for validation, particularly comparing data from different systems, in the Casemix Management system. Ideally such validation of data takes place in the operational environment.

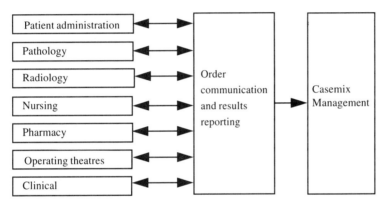

Figure 39. System configuration: on implementation of order communications/results reporting

Where an order communications and results reporting system has been implemented within the hospital there are not only operational advantages but also advantages in the provision of management information to the Casemix Management system. Events are linked to patients at the operational level and therefore any discrepancies are resolved where they are spotted and where there is an operational reason to improve the data. Also, there is only one (or at least a smaller number) of different links between the different systems making the whole process of implementation quicker, easier and cheaper (see Figure 39).

But again, this scenario is only one step towards the comprehensive operational and management information systems required to support the work of the hospital and contribute towards improved patient care which might be characterised as shown in Figure 40.

It will take most hospitals many years before such an integrated range of information systems support is available to support both operational and management processes. The start of this process is the development of an information systems strategy for the hospital. This document, based on the business objectives of the hospital, provides the answers to three questions concerning information and information systems:

- Where are we now?
- Where do we want to be in the future?
- How do we get there?

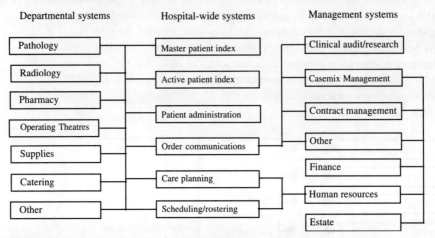

Figure 40. System configuration: integrated range of systems

Type of computer system

But back to the present time.

While the design of the Casemix Management system is relatively simple, it contains a great deal of data which needs to be analysed in a variety of ways. For this reason, most of the systems available run on mid-range or mini-computers.

The ease of use and graphical presentation required is more appropriate using microcomputers and the software that is designed for these computers. Some systems will 'download' or transfer data to microcomputers for analysis and presentation. Others will use 'co-operative processing' which means that some of the system will run on the central computer and some on microcomputers but this is transparent to the person using the system.

The Casemix Management system itself is relatively simple. What makes it so powerful is the manner in which the data can be analysed and presented. The reporting system provided is therefore an extremely important element. Some suppliers will say that data can be downloaded into any of the popular microcomputer program that you may already be using. Others will provide an excellent reporting program but will state that since it is so good and user friendly the user can define the reports that meet the precise requirements. Both approaches are only partially satisfactory and may well amount to a 'cop out' on the part of the supplier.

7. Care profiles

What are care profiles?

Care profiles are the key to successful use of Casemix Management information. They describe the expected process of care or treatment for a group of patients. Table 16 shows a basic profile for the patient group: Primary replacement of major joints.

Primary replacement of major joints			
Length of stay		Pathology	
average	19 days	simple biochemistry	7 tests
minimum	10 days	simple haematology	7 tests
maximum	25 days	simple histology	1 test
Theatres		simple microbiology	7 tests
major	1.5 hours	Nursing	
Radiology		qualified	29 hours
simple	9 films	unqualified	28 hours
complex	1 film	Other services	
Pharmacy		other services	50 hours
Pharmacy	345 doses	Expected cost	£1,713.00

Table 16. Care profile

The care profile defines the expected care for patients falling into a particular group in terms of diagnostic or therapeutic interventions that take place during the episode of care, similar to the way in which data is held on individual patient records. Care profiles can be costed by reference to the standard cost tables of events.

The groups are defined in such a way that patients falling within the group are clinically coherent and consume similar resources. That is, a patient falling into the group elicits a similar clinical response in terms of the investigations ordered and the treatment given and consequently exhibits a similar cost. Because an individual profile may contain patients with various diagnoses and since all patients are different, the expected treatment will vary to a degree. Individual profiles may also contain patients with the same diagnosis but with different treatment protocols.

Some items may be defined as a range. Table 16 shows length of stay defined as a range, with the minimum, maximum and expected length of stay specified. For costing purposes, the average figure will be used. For identifying records which lie outside the profile, the minimum and maximum figures may be used.

Other items may be defined as a proportion. For example, 70 per cent of patients within the group may be expected to undergo one type of radiological investigation, 25 per cent another and five per cent none at all.

The patient groups for which a profile is defined are carefully selected in order that they are clinically and resource coherent. However, other aspects also need to be considered when setting profiles.

Several sets of profiles may be defined within the system for different purposes. For example, a management set will be defined which allows linkage to structures and processes and is used for monitoring purposes. Further sets may be defined to model a future period, and others for medical or clinical audit studies.

The management set of profiles needs to be defined in a way that allows further grouping to match the management structure of the hospital and linkage to budgets and to contracts. Furthermore, these profiles need to be defined so that all patients fall into one and only one group.

Profiles defined for audit studies are likely to be defined at a greater level of detail than those defined for general management processes. At this level, patients may fall into more than one group or may not be included in any defined gorup, in which case profiles can be defined on an *ad hoc* basis for audit, research or investigating alternative profiles of care.

Profiles used at management level, for example by clinical directors, should also cover all aspects of patient care. In the early stage there may be many events such as physiotherapy, medications, ECG, EEG, etc., which are not individually recorded against the patient record. In order to use the information to link to budgets and contracts, these elements may be recorded as an additional apportioned cost related either to the particular patient group, to a day of stay or to an attendance. This could be the same for all patients or made more specific by patient group, ward, specialty or to other factor where the differential use of resources can be determined.

Care profiles and protocols

Care profiles should not be confused with treatment protocols. They are very different in nature. Treatment protocols are more detailed and relate to a much smaller group of patients and are used as a basis for the treatment of individual patients and formulation of their care plans. Other terms that are increasingly being used include accelerated recovery pathways and personal order sets. The standard protocol is modified to provide the treatment protocol or care plan for an individual patient against which the actual treatment of that individual patient may be monitored. The way in which these protocols are defined is very different from care profiles and can indeed be a lengthy process.

A care profile is described in less detail than a protocol. It may be derived from summarising of a protocol. However, protocols cannot be derived from profiles since sufficient detail is not available.

Why are care profiles important?

At the clinical level, profiles can be a powerful tool for use in the audit process. Patients whose actual activity varied from that which was expected can be identified and further investigated, for example all patients who should have had a particular investigation but did not, or all patients meeting specified criteria. These criteria may be characteristics of the patients themselves, for example age, of their problem, for example diagnosis, or of their investigation and treatment.

Profiles can also be used to monitor statistical distributions. For example, the expected percentage of nosocomial infections might be specified in a profile and the actual percentage of infections, and the significance of this measured against it. In such cases, it is not possible to identify individual patients falling outside the criteria of the profile but only the level or distribution within the group as a whole.

Care profiles are the key to linking the casemix information to some of the major management processes of the hospital. They allow the definition of an expected process of care for different patient groups and consequently the expected cost of patients within each group. Combined with the expected number of patients in each group, this then indicates the total expected activity and hence cost of each specialty, budget, contract or any other group of patients. This is extremely useful at the planning, negotiating and setting stages of the budgeting and contracting processes.

Once set, the actual activity can be compared with that which was expected, and large amounts of information monitored by determining variation of actual activity (and cost) from that which was expected, negotiated or planned.

The sequence shown in Figure 41 illustrates how a single set of profiles can be linked to management structures and to the processes of contracting and budgeting.

Increasingly elements of the service department budgets are allocated to clinical teams. Different elements of the budget may be allocated to different budget holders, for example fixed costs to the service department and variable costs of the clinical team. The information can be used to monitor such budgets so long as the different elements of standard cost such as fixed and variable, direct and indirect are defined. Figure 42 shows how the pathology events defined on the profile, and costed giving separate fixed and variable elements, may be allocated to the Pathology department and to the clinical team budgets.

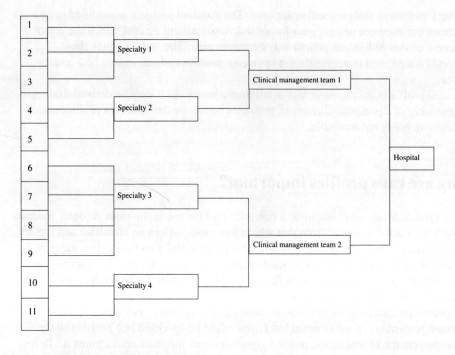

Figure 41. Linking profiles to budgets

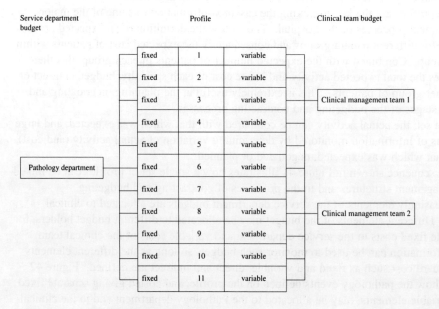

Figure 42. Linking profiles to budgets

The core Casemix Management system is not a budgetary system but requires very close links with it. Some of the more sophisticated systems do have fully functional budgetary systems within them and are intended to be used as such.

The expected numbers of cases, casemix and process of care can be taken into consideration during the budget negotiation and contract negotiation processes (see Figure 43). There is little point setting budgets or contracts which do not relate directly to the expected clinical activity that will or can be generated. The use of information from the Casemix Management system can make this negotiation process more precise and reduce the risk. It also allows the process of quality to be incorporated into the negotiations.

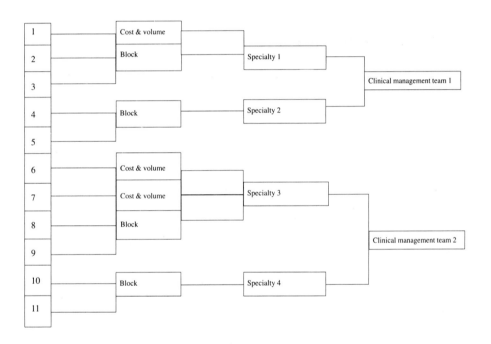

Figure 43. Linking profiles to contracts

The negotiation revolves around the process for a group of patients, the expected numbers in each group and the funds available, or those which can be generated through the contracting process. The level of particular resources available, and any known pressures on resources, for example shortage of theatre time, will be taken into account. Clinicians must be allowed to set the process element on the basis that different processes may adversely affect the quality of patient care. The casemix, or numbers of patients in different groups, can be varied to a certain extent within the funding that is available.

The 'what if' modelling capabilities of the systems allows the implications of varying processes of care and numbers of patients to be assessed before budgets and contracts are agreed. The risk associated with any one contract can be modelled by:

- Applying different numbers of patients to each profile defined within the set for each contract.
- Applying different but valid process of care definitions to profiles defined within the set for each contract.

In this way the risk and sensitivity of particular variations on each contract can be determined. Particularly sensitive groups can be monitored more closely than those where change has little impact on the contract.

How are care profiles constructed?

It has often been suggested that setting profiles is a lengthy process. In some instances, it can be, but this time may be significantly reduced. If the process is started with a blank sheet of paper and attempts are made to establish the expected process for a patient in a particular group, it does take a long time, may provide a wide range of responses and bear little relation to what is actually happening.

The easiest and quickest way in which to set profiles is to capture actual data within the Casemix Management system for a period of, say, three to six months, analyse this data by patient group and set this as the initial profiles. That is, set the profiles initially to what is actually happening. This has the added advantage of being able to measure the actual coherence of the group in advance of using profiles to identify and report variation. This may identify groups which may need to be divided or combined in order to provide a more effective basis for monitoring. What is actually happening is not, however, necessarily what the clinicians would consider to be appropriate. Through discussions with clinicians, the profiles can be modified to reflect the desired position. Also at this stage quality standards may be built into the process. In some hospitals, the definition of profiles is seen as an appropriate part of the medical audit meetings.

Once budgets and contracts are linked to the defintion of profiles, care must be taken as to how and when the management set of profiles are changed, since any changes mean that the expected activity and cost you are monitoring against may no longer reflect the budgets and contracts negotiated and set.

Changing care profiles

Care profiles are a key element in the plans against which actual events are monitored. They are used to monitor actual activity and cost against what actually happened. It is important that changes to care profiles, and hence changes to plans, are restricted to particular people within the organisation, and that changes are notified to all those who have a need to know.

8. Costing

Costing principles

In April 1993, the Director of Finance and Corporate Information at the NHS Executive issued guidance on the principles and approach for cost allocation as it applied to the contracting process.[35] This executive letter pointed out
that a great deal of progress had been made in the development of the contracting process but that 'the lack of valid, reliable and comparative data is the weak link in the contracting process'. It indicated that purchasers should expect a 'professional and reasonably consistent approach to costing by all providers' and an agreement on the contract categories to be used. The guidance provides 'a minimum level of sophistication in cost allocation' but is not intended to stop those providers who can use more sophisticated costing methods from doing so. It reiterated the basic established financial principles: [36,37]

- Prices should be based on costs.
- Costs should be established on a full-cost basis.
- There should be no planned cross-subsidisation between specialties, procedures or contracts.

The new approach was set out in 'Cost Allocation General Principles and Approach for 1993/1994'. This document sets out minimum standards for costing. It:

- Provides descriptions of different elements of cost; direct, indirect, overhead, fixed, semi-fixed and variable.
- Sets out the recommendations of the National Steering Group on Costing as to how individual costs should be allocated to these headings.
- Proposes how costs should be allocated.

Casemix systems hold costs at the level of an individual event. In order to derive these event costs, the total costs of the hospital are apportioned according to a defined model. For example, the costs of pathology tests will not only include the direct costs of the Pathology department, such as the staff, equipment and consumables, but also a proportion of the general overheads of running the hospital, for example administration and cleaning. This is known as a 'top-down' approach. Having derived a cost for each of the events, patient costs are then derived using a 'bottom-up' approach; summing the cost of all events for individual patients.

Since not all events are captured individually on the patient record, some of the costs will be apportioned, for example to a patient episode, bed day or attendance. Costs such as catering and domestic are more appropriately apportioned to bed day, whereas physiotherapy may be more appropriately apportioned to episode. Each of these costs may be specific to individual specialties, wards, patient groups or other factors.

It should be remembered that the costing process itself can be a costly business. It is therefore important that each hospital considers what is an appropriate level of detail at which to cost. For example, it may be considered appropriate to determine the level of cost of a pathology test by taking the total cost of the Pathology department, including overheads, and dividing this by the total number of tests; each test having the same standard cost. At the other extreme, the cost of each test can be determined from the staff time required for the test and cost of consumables. The appropriate level will be somewhere in-between, perhaps grouping tests in a limited number of bands, each of which is costed.

The Casemix Management system, as a minimum, should be able to hold costs split into the separate elements, at the level of individual event. The importance of the different elements was discussed when considering information to support budgeting and internal trading. But what do these mean? The relationship between the different elements of cost and activity is illustrated in Figure 44.

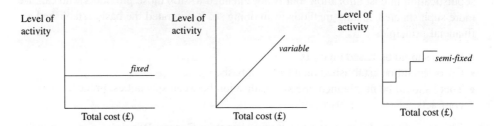

Figure 44. Fixed, variable and semi-fixed costs

Fixed costs are those which do not change with changes in the level of activity over a defined period, normally one year. Many staff are included in this category: consultant medical staff, senior nursing staff, student and pupil nurses as well as costs such as rates, depreciation, capital charges, and engineering and building maintenance.

Variable costs are those that vary in proportion to the level of activity. A change in activity results in a proportionate change in cost. Variable costs will include drugs, medical gases, dressings, and laboratory and radiology materials.

Semi-fixed costs remain fixed over a range of activities but then change in 'step' manner when activity rises to or falls below a specific level. They then remain fixed until the next 'trigger' point in activity is reached. For example, if inpatient activity decreases sufficiently, less nurses are required, but this is likely only to apply if a whole ward is closed. Nurses, junior medical staff, professional and technical staff, clerical staff, maintenance contracts, laundry and telephone rentals are included in this category.

Some of the early UK systems held cost data on each patient record. This was found to be unnecessary and takes up a great deal of disc storage. This is one of the reasons why early systems required such large computers to run on at consequently higher cost. Most systems hold costs in cost tables. Costs are attached to patient records or profiles during the reporting process. This is more efficient in terms of use of the computer but does make reporting a little more difficult.

Where are costs calculated?

Standard costs may be calculated within the casemix system itself. Some systems allow you to use a variety of costing methods and also to hold more than one cost for an event. This is particularly true of some of the systems originating in the US where the costing aspects can be quite sophisticated.

Standard costs may be calculated within a modern general ledger system and transferred to the Casemix Management system. This has the advantage that the monitoring of standard costs against actual is easier.

Some systems will accept costs, together with the patient and event details, from the feeder systems. This can conflict when holding costs in costs tables.

Costs may also be calculated in a separate costing system. This can be as simple as a spreadsheet with the data being transferred to the Casemix Management system as required. A number of such systems were reviewed in a document produced by the National Steering Group on Costing in 1992.

The first two methods are to be preferred because of the control they give over the data and the ability to monitor more easily. Some kind of link to the financial accounting system, particularly the general ledger, is crucial for maintaining consistency between the costing component of the management accounting system and the aggregate financial position of the hospital.

How frequently are standard costs changed?

The simple answer is 'as little as possible and as often as necessary'. Ideally, standard costs are only changed once a year. This way users have a stable environment in which to work. However, in the early stages it may be necessary to change costs more frequently. Also, costs of different events may need to be changed at different times of the year, particularly those which have a large element of staff costs.

Costs are a key element in using casemix information to monitor budgets and contracts. As such the authorisation to be able to change event costs needs to be restricted.

Implementation issues of costing

There are a number of implementation issues that need to be added in relation to costing:

How are overheads to be apportioned? Some will relate to each day of a patient's stay, for example cleaning and catering. Some costs will relate to the patient episode, for example portering. How do you apportion cleaning of an overhead department such as administration or finance as opposed to an operational area such as pathology or a direct care area such as a ward? These are important questions which need to be faced as costing becomes more sophisticated. The commercial sector, such as large manufacturing companies, which need fine detail on product costs (their equivalent of episode costs), have been wrestling with these problems for many years. The NHS has only just begun. At the time of going to print, there is no standard method used throughout the UK.

Initially, it is unlikely that all direct patient events will be captured in detail since this requires the existence of a comprehensive range of operational systems currently found in few hospitals. Will these costs be allocated on the basis of patient episode or by casemix group or both?

If casemix information is to be used as part of the budget negotiation and management process, it is important that the standard costs within casemix can be reconciled with the actual costs within the hospital's general ledger. Unless one of the more sophisticated Casemix Management systems has been procured, it is likely that a different system will be used to provide budget statements. If this is the case, it is necessary to be able to reconcile the casemix information with that provided by the budget reporting system.

A costing strategy is required which provides answers to these questions.

9. Reporting

Characteristics

The Casemix Management system consists of a large repository of data, containing individual patient records including events which can be grouped in all manner of different ways, care profiles defining the expected process of care for groups of patients, and costs at the level of individual event that can be used to cost both expected and actual care.

None of this is any use at all unless clinicians and managers can access the information when they need it, analyse it the way they want and present it in a form that makes it easy to interpret.

This is the job of the reporting part of the system, which is therefore of crucial importance to the success of the system, being able to support the objectives and processes of the organisation. Both the tools themselves and the way in which they are implemented are important. This is often a weak part of the system for a number of reasons which may include:

- The range of reports readily available does not provide the required information.
- Reports are not structured in any logical manner or are all at the same level.
- The tools available to construct required reports are too difficult to use.
- Information is not available on timescale required, for example only available overnight.
- Equipment needed to access information is not in a convenient location.
- Tables only (not graphics) are available, making interpretation time consuming and difficult.

These are just some of the reasons why information is not used. All of these problems can be overcome.

The following characteristics should be present:

- Reporting (both paper and screen output) and enquiry (regular and one-off) capabilities.
- The ability to define and save reports that will be run on a regular basis.
- Easy to use data enquiry to allow all users to meet many of their *ad hoc* information requirements without having to resort to programming.
- The ability to structure reports so they can be easily located and viewed in the sequence appropriate to the role of an individual user.

83

- High quality graphical presentation which may be viewed on a computer screen or printed out. Colour aids interpretation of the information. The normal range of business graphics should be available as well as producing reports in tabular form.
- Sophisticated data analysis and presentation facilities to allow the more technical user to carry out complex analyses and to support other users for their more complex requirements.
- The ability to quickly flip from a graphical view to the table of figures making up the graph.
- It is an advantage to be able to see a number of reports on the screen at the same time.

In addition, it is essential that proactive support is available to ensure that clinicians and managers have the information they require, know how to interpret that information appropriately and ensure that the information available meets changing requirements.

Tools

A single tool for analysing and presenting information is unlikely to meet all requirements of those who want information from a management information system. There is a requirement for clinicians and managers to be able to view pre-defined reports quickly and without the need to learn complex instructions to define their own reports. Such tools are known as 'Graphical User Interfaces' (GUIs) or 'Executive Information Systems' (EISs). These tools will not normally allow the definition of complex reports, for which a Report Generator is required. It will normally require considerable skill and practice to use such tools effectively. A few people will want to define and run complex models and may require a specialised modelling tool to do this. This section looks at the first of these; the GUI or EIS.

There is a wide range of tools which meet the reporting requirements, all of which provide slightly different facilities. It is hardly surprising that there is confusion when procuring such tools. Just some of those that might be considered are EPIC, Executive Eagle, HOLOS, Business Objects, Track, Acuity, Empower, Gentium and Lightship. While many of these are known as Executive Information Systems, the ease of use for viewing information offered by these products is required by all non-technical users of the system, not only those in an executive position. The price of the products does not always reflect this need.

Whatever tools are used, the supplier or in-house technical support will need to set up the regular reports and provide an *ad hoc* reporting service and a maintenance and development service as the requirements for reporting change. If the system is to continue to meet the requirements of the organisation, the reports required on a regular basis will change frequently. Objectives and issues will change and the ability of the user to use more complex analyses will improve. This support requirement may change the roles of some people in the organisation and training will certainly be required by all involved. An easy to approach, friendly and co-operative support group, or information centre, can be crucial to ongoing enhancement of system use. These roles are often difficult for traditional data processing staff to adopt as they require a significant cultural shift from 'expert' to 'supporter'.

Standard versus *ad hoc* reporting

There is a lot of misunderstanding about standard and *ad hoc* reporting. Some of the suppliers say they provide a good set of tools that are easy to use and the user can define their own reports. This is often a substitute for the supplier understanding how their system may be used most effectively and providing the reports that are required. Standard reporting does not need to be the reams of paper produced by computer systems of the past. The reports were rarely looked at and did not provide exactly the information required. A modern standard report may be a single graph displayed on the screen. If it is required regularly it should be included in the routine set of standard reports and generated automatically at the required frequency. Defined in such terms, it is likely that some 700–900 reports will be required by the average hospital system in order to meet routine monitoring requirements alone. This is very different from the 20–50 reports often provided by suppliers on delivery of the system. This gives some indication of the implementation and support effort that is required to provide users with the information they require.

The aim should be to move towards standard or parameterised reporting while still retaining the facility to create *ad hoc* reports when required. Reports should not swamp the user with information but be tightly focused to give the user the information required without substantial further manual analysis. Over time, some reports will no longer be needed; these should be removed or archived to prevent difficulty in obtaining useful information.

Range of presentation graphics

The range of presentation graphics required is not complex and is satisfied by those available in most business graphics packages. The pie chart, bar chart, stacked bar chart and line graph are essentials. Scattergrams and XY charts can present in such a way as might otherwise require tables or two or more charts to provide the same information. Control charts are particularly useful when wanting to monitor activity and cost within a range, for example when monitoring key aspects of the process of treatment for a group of patients.

Typical uses of different types of chart are shown in Figures 45-50.

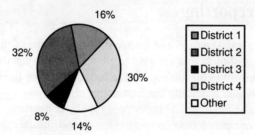

Figure 45. Pie chart

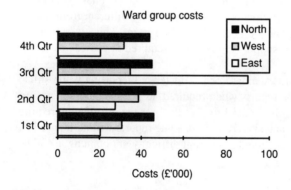

Figure 46 Bar chart

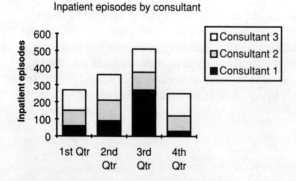

Figure 47. Stacked column chart

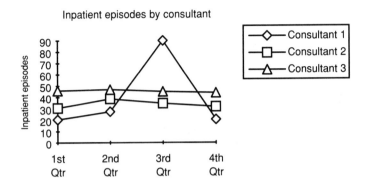

Figure 48. Line graph: trend analysis

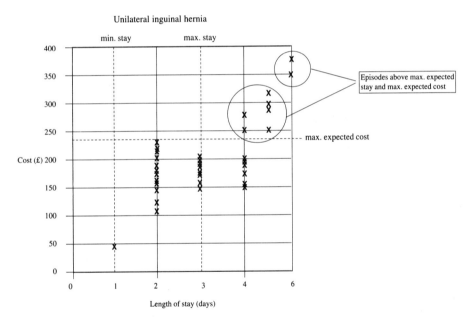

Figure 49. XY chart : scattergram

Structuring the reports

For routine monitoring it is important to be able to review quickly key indicators which show whether things are going as expected or not. No manager has the time to wade through reams of reports only to find out that all is well. When things are not going as expected, further information on the relevant topic needs to be easily available in order to investigate the issue. Casemix information allows this tracking right down to the level of individual patients, if necessary.

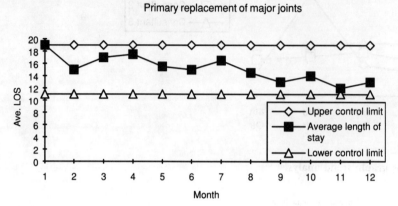

Figure 50. Control chart

Level 1 reports	Level 2 reports	Level 3 reports
For hospital (corporate users)		
By clinical team	By specialty within clinical team	By service within specialty within clinical team
	By service within clinical team	
	By purchaser within clinical team	By contract within purchaser within clinical team
	By contract within clinical team	
By service	By clinical team within service	By specialty within service within clinical team
By purchaser	By contract within purchaser	
For each clinical team		
By specialty	By service within specialty	By consultant within specialty within service
By service	By specialty within service	By consultant within specialty within service
By casemix group	By diagnosis within casemix group	
	Length of inpatient stay within casemix group	Length of stay by consultant within casemix group
	Episodes by grouped cost	Episodes by grouped cost by consultant
By purchaser	By contract within purchaser	By consultant within contract within purchaser

Table 17. Menu structure for reports

88

To be most effective, reports need to be tailored to the roles, responsibilities and issues that an individual is concerned with at the time. For routine processes, a consistency of reports needs to be maintained throughout the organisation.

Table 17 shows how the menu might be structured to give routine monitoring reports for activity and cost.

Each of these reports might be available in a number of formats, as appropriate to the individual report, such as:

- Actual and expected.
- Variation from expected.
- Percentage variation from expected.
- Treatment, volume, casemix variation.
- Various time periods:
  ◊ Last month.
  ◊ Last year.
  ◊ Current year to date.
  ◊ Projected end of year.
  ◊ Monthly trend over 12 months.
- Various graphical displays:
  ◊ Bar chart, column chart.
  ◊ Pie.
  ◊ Line graph.
  ◊ Combined bar or column and line graph.
- Tables behind the graphics.
- Text comment attached to any tables or graphics.

Graphical user interface / executive information system, specification checklist

An aspect to be considered when procuring a Graphical User Interface or Executive Information System is to provide users with easy access to the information they require. While this is an extensive list and all aspects need to be considered, this is *not* intended to imply that an extensive requirements document is necessarily drawn up to which suppliers must respond in detail and in writing. The more it costs a supplier to sell the product, the more that product will cost. Common sense should be applied based on the anticipated value of any resulting contract.

- Users and use:
  ◊ Who is expected to use the system: role, numbers and locations? Consider:
    ° Clinical directors.
    ° Business managers.
    ° Directorate information and finance resources.
    ° Nurse managers.

    °   Service department managers.
    °   Audit co-ordinators.
    °   Clinicians.
    °   Corporate directors.
    °   Corporate information and finance resources.

- Presentation formats:
  ◊ Graphics: bar charts, line charts, scattergrams, pie charts, X-Y charts, combined charts (e.g. bar and line), geographical (maps), control charts, Gantt charts, network diagrams.
  ◊ Are two and three dimensional graphics required?
  ◊ Will all display screens be in colour or is presentation on monochrome screens required (not recommended)?
  ◊ How many colours can be displayed?
  ◊ Can all graphical reports (including those in colour) be printed in black and white and with adequate resolution of grey scales?
  ◊ Text: plain text information, standard help text, user help text, textual annotation of graphics and tables.
  ◊ Tables: maximum rows, maximum columns, scrolling over more than one screen.
  ◊ Other types of presentation: simple diagrams (boxes, lines, circles), photographic images, sound, video, clip art.
  ◊ Exception reports with graphic or text display dependent on user defined value of variables.
  ◊ Changing format or colour of graphic or text display dependent on value of variable.

- Features:
  ◊ Viewing pre-defined reports.
  ◊ User definition of simple *ad hoc* reports.
  ◊ Definition of more complex *ad hoc* reports.
  ◊ Browsing data in database.
  ◊ Creating menus, reports, graphics (user features as opposed to application development).
  ◊ Ability to scroll and page tables, text and graphics (where these would not fit on a single screen).
  ◊ User calculation of additional data items (i.e. additional to application development).
  ◊ Modelling and/or projecting.
  ◊ Statistical analysis (e.g. means of indicating statistical significance on a variation chart or calculation of statistics, Chi, standard deviation, various significance etc.).
  ◊ Ability to annotate and send reports elsewhere.
  ◊ Incorporating tables, graphics from this product into other applications (e.g. taking a barchart and inputting into a word processing document).
     °   Technical development and support staff.

◊ Can you view more than one report on the screen at any one time?
- Navigation aids:
  ◊ Drill down.
  ◊ Menu choices.
  ◊ Point and click.
  ◊ Command buttons.
  ◊ Hot spots on tables and graphics.
  ◊ Map of reporting hierarchy.
    ° Indication of current position in reporting hierarchy.
- Time periods for reporting:
  ◊ Last month.
  ◊ Last year.
  ◊ Current year to date; calendar or financial.
  ◊ Projected end of year; calendar or financial.
  ◊ Monthly over past year.
  ◊ Quarterly over past two years.
- Technical environment:
  ◊ Preferred operating environment - hardware standards (processors, printers), software standards (operating systems), network standards.
  ◊ Anticipated data distribution across personal computers, fileservers and larger computers.
  ◊ Requirement for automatic update of databases on regular basis via network.
  ◊ Whether and how a distributed database might function and how this might provide seamless access to the user.
  ◊ Sources of data including hardware and software environments.
  ◊ Whether and how the product can facilitate automatic update from extraction of data from data sources, transfer across network and update of database.
  ◊ Whether and how the product can provide direct access to source databases for *ad hoc* analysis.
    ° Minimum specification for each of the relevant technical environments in which their product operates, e.g. minimum specification of personal computers, operating system or additional software required.
- Security:
  ◊ Password access.
  ◊ Ability for users to change own password.
  ◊ Protected access to parts of database.
  ◊ Facilities to aid back-up and restore.
  ◊ Protection of data from change or delete.
- Application development:
  ◊ If in-house application development intended:
    ° Licence implications of local development.
    ° Training requirements for application's developers.
    ° Training provision for application's developers: nature, duration, location, cost.

- °   Assistance and support available from supplier (including costs).
- ◊ Facilities available to developers:
  - °   Creation of business graphics: control of colours, headings, axis titles, legends.
  - °   Creation of tables: column/row headings, column width, text and number formatting, number of columns, number of rows, column width, typeface, font size, decimal places, display of negative values, colour coding dependent on value.
  - °   Assistance to testing of application.
- ◊ If supplier expected to develop the application:
  - °   Realistic effort and costs to be incurred by supplier.
  - °   Local knowledge and time required to input to process.
- ● User training:
  - ◊ Training required by users.
  - ◊ Supplier provision of training for users: nature, duration, location, cost.
- ● Support / documentation:
  - ◊ What support is required and provided, e.g. hot lines?
  - ◊ What documentation is provided with the product: for users and application developers?
- ● Outline of report model:
  - ◊ What reports are required for which users and how are these to be hierarchically structured?
- ● Costs:
  - ◊ How much will the product cost for the number of anticipated users?
    - °   Software licences: user and development.
    - °   Training: user, application development.
    - °   Support: user, application development.
    - °   Upgrade policy.
  - ◊ Cost of other hardware and software products required:
    - °   Upgrade to existing or new personal computers.
    - °   Upgrade to existing file servers, central processors or networks.
    - °   Upgrade to existing or new systems or applications software.
    - °   Upgrade to existing or new printers.
- ● Company/product profile; particularly if considering application development or extensive support from the supplier:
  - ◊ Company: size, turnover, client list (for product under consideration).
  - ◊ Product: background history including when first released.
  - ◊ Independent reviews of product.

10. Identifying and realising benefits

Benefits of management information systems

Benefits of hospital management information systems derive from:

- Understanding better the services provided by the organisation: what is provided, to whom, how and at what cost.
- Measuring actual activity and cost against that which is expected as expressed by contracts, budgets, plans and profiles.
- Providing opportunities for change in clinical and general management processes in order to improve patient care, as a result of information being available to support such changes, and to identify the need for supporting such changes.
- Being able to predict the possible consequences of intended changes to services provided.
- Making more efficient use of the information resource to support users of the information, for example by defining more routine or parameterised reports allowing support staff to focus on new and more sophisticated requirements.

In order to derive these benefits, the information must be *useful, usable* and *used*. Information must be used appropriately if it is to inform and improve the decision-making processes. Benefits will not be derived automatically. They need to be worked at, continuously.

Ensuring that the information is *useful*

If the information is to be useful, those who will use that information must be involved in defining the content and structure of the reports that they will use. They must also be involved in defining key elements of the data: patient groups, profiles, expected numbers of cases and costs.

The scope and detail of the base data must be appropriate to support the processes for which it is being used, including the:

- Patients included within the system: inpatients, outpatients, all.
- Individual patient events included within the system.
- Level of detail and coverage of event costing.

- Clinical and resource coherence of the patient groups used.
- Coverage and detail of profiles.

Ensuring that the information is *usable*:

The system can only be considered usable if users have easy access to the information, in a form that is easy to understand and interpret and matched to their level of information skills and willingness to use information. This requires a range of tools allowing access of information through a few keystrokes to simple graphics and tables to advanced modelling for information experts.

The data must be accurate. Comprehensive data audit will ensure that users can have confidence in the information and that accuracy and coverage of the data is appropriate to the purposes for which it is being used.

Ensuring that the information is *used* appropriately:

No matter how well the system is designed and implemented, benefits will only arise if the information is used by clinical and general managers as part of the decision-making processes. Unlike an operational system, there is no imperative for users to use the system. Such an operational imperative would be, for example, the need to enter a Pathology order for a patient into a system in order that the request is made. Use of the system is essential for improvement of patient care, in general, in the medium or longer term and for survival of the 'business'. Benefits will only be derived if managers want to use the system and this is only achieved if:

- There is a sense of ownership of the system by all users.
- Individual users understand the benefits that will be derived by them, personally, through use of the information.
- Individual users understand what information is available, how it might be used as part of processes that they are involved in and how it can be interpreted appropriately.
- Using information is part of the 'culture' of the hospital.

Potential benefits

The benefit from appropriate use of the information can be summarised in a single statement:

'Improved ability of clinical and general managers to determine and meet their objectives.'

Reasons often stated for the purchase of an information system are that it should

94

improve the quality and reduce the cost of patient care. Management information systems will directly achieve neither of these aims. If individuals' objectives include the improvement of quality or reduction of cost, then the information will contribute to improving the quality and reducing the cost of patient care.

The following lists some of the benefits that can be achieved by a hospital through the use of patient-based management information systems. All use of the information is targeted at improving patient care and clinical practice through the support of clinical and general management processes.

- **Corporate management**
  - ◊ Corporate management will consistently obtain earlier and more explicit warning of major deviations from planned patterns of service.
  - ◊ Structured information will provide a common, agreed basis for communication between adjacent tiers of the management structure.
  - ◊ Corporate management will have information which will assist in maximising income from purchasers.
- **All managers**
  - ◊ Managers will monitor key service indicators on a regular basis, linked to their own sphere of responsibility, and understand what action they will take when these indicators change.
  - ◊ Managers will monitor activity, quality and cost, linked to their own sphere of responsibility and in relation to measures of expectation defined in contracts, budgets, profiles and targets, and understand what action they will take when variation is identified. Volume, treatment and casemix variations will be readily available.
  - ◊ Managers will understand the level of service provision, within their sphere of responsibility, to individual purchasers and within individual contracts.
  - ◊ Managers will better understand activity and cost within their area of responsibility in relation to patient groups and services provided as derived from care provided to individuals.
  - ◊ Managers will be able to predict activity and cost for subsequent years related to patient groups, services provided, practitioner groups and care locations based on past activity and estimations of future activity. This will improve the ability of clinical managers to take a full and effective part in planning, contracting and budgeting activities.
  - ◊ The information will assist managers in identifying areas of opportunity for service development and identify areas where resources would be beneficially reallocated.
- **Service providers**
  - ◊ Better understanding of their provision of service to individual Clinical Directorates and sensitivity to changes in the mix of cases within these directorates.
- **Directorate management**
  - ◊ Information about services, for example pathology, provided to specific clinical

95

directorates, will facilitate the introduction of service level agreements and internal trading arrangements.

◊ Clinical managers will be able to highlight areas of clinical activity which are appropriate for the hospital to develop and those areas where activity should cease. In particular, such areas might relate to the ability of the hospital to provide a competitive service in relation to other providers, whether for reasons of quantity, quality or cost. Such changes would be negotiated through the contracting process.

◊ Information on resources consumed and process of care by particular patient groups will assist clinical managers in reviewing which services to put forward.

◊ Comparative information on activity, process, outcome and cost, related to individual consultants and clinically coherent patient groups will allow analysis of performance.

● **Clinicians**

◊ Clinicians will, increasingly, have access to a summary list of all events, e.g. Pathology tests, of individual patients and the cost of their care.

◊ Clinicians will be able to identify cases to be included in specific audit studies.

◊ Clinicians will be able to set process profiles for specific audit studies and routinely measure actual activity against these profiles in order to improve the process of patient care.

◊ Clinicians will be able to review major exceptions to expected patterns of care.

◊ Clinicians will be able to audit the clinical and resource coherence of patient groups in order to continually refine the measures of expectation and hence reduce the risks inherent in the contracting process. Such risks are associated, for example, with drift towards more complex cases within single groups.

● **Information staff**

◊ Information staff time will be released from the production of the *ad hoc* reports to be reallocated to providing the more sophisticated support to users required as part of the implementation of the system.

Methods for realising benefits

A number of different techniques can contribute to a overall programme of benefits identification and realisation.

Benefits statement approach

This approach relies on the development of measurable statements of benefit against which achievements can be determined. These statements will be based on the objectives of the organisation and of the individual clinical and general managers. Brainstorming sessions and workshops, involving these users of the information and supported by expert facilitators are used to identify the statements of benefit that each individual intends to pursue. It is essential that the individuals who will achieve the benefit define their own statements; statements set by others and imposed will be ignored.

The earlier section, Potential benefits, identified in some broad statements the potential benefits available. These can be used as the basis for defining more detailed and statements. The statement should be described in terms that can be measured using the available information. Each statement is associated with:

- A baseline which defines the level which is currently being achieved.
- A target, which defines what is intended to be achieved over what timescale.
- Reports required to monitor progress towards the target.

If appropriate, the targets may be included within the information system in the form of profiles of care or expected numbers of cases.

It is essential that the targets, set for the purpose of realising benefits, are not used for other management purposes, for example assessing performance. Should this happen, there will be an understandable reluctance for individuals to set challenging targets for the achievement of benefit.

Problem-oriented approach

In this approach the focus is on how the information may be used to investigate and resolve current issues and problems. Identification and discussion of problems and issues provides an opportunity to determine how information will contribute to their resolution. A preliminary step in this approach is to recognise that the perception of the problem or issue may be different in different parts of the organisation. All those whose actions lead to the definition and resolution are ideally identified and included in the process.

Multi-disciplinary workshops will focus on particular problems and issues and determine the information that will assist in their further investigation and resolution. In a similar manner to the benefit statement approach, baselines will be defined, targets set and achievements monitored.

Anecdotal evidence

Benefits will be derived which are not identified through the formal processes. These will derive from users exploring the information and, with expert support, interpreting that information in innovative and unexpected ways. This is entirely appropriate from the introduction of a management information system and should be encouraged. Workshop sessions may discuss ways in which information has been used, what benefits have been derived and how this knowledge may be used or adapted by other users of the system to derive additional benefit. A more individual approach may be more successful in some hospitals. Responsibility may be allocated, perhaps within Information Support, for someone to regularly discuss with users their need for and use of information. Benefits identified in this way may be described and demonstrated to others.

Transferring knowledge of benefits

Transfer of knowledge of benefits has already been mentioned above. This process should be formalised by the introduction of benefits transfer through normal management processes. These might include training courses, lunch-time meetings, management clubs, newsletters or other features of the local management culture.

Benefit example

Medicine outpatient audit

This example is of the use of information to support a medicine outpatient audit. The aim of the audit was to study outpatient working patterns with the intention of continuously improving them.

The first stage was to identify key indicators and measure their current levels. Information was collected for the first appointment and review appointments within six months. The information used was:

- Length of time between referral and clinic appointment for new patients.
- Proportion of outpatients seen by consultants.
- Number of investigations ordered.
- At which appointment a diagnosis was made.

Following initial investigations, targets were set and progress towards targets regularly monitored. Recommendations included:

- Maximum waiting time set to first appointment.
- All new outpatients seen by either a consultant or senior registrar.
- Higher priority given to clearly stating a firm diagnosis or opinion.

Regular reports were defined and made available to monitor achievements on a regular basis:

- Distribution of waiting times.
- List of patients whose waiting time exceeded the maximum.
- Numbers of new patients not seen by a consultant or senior registrar.
- List of new outpatients who were not seen by a consultant or senior registrar.
- Proportion of patients with coded diagnosis or problem by sequence number of attendance.
- List of patients without coded diagnosis or problem.

By viewing distributions, numbers and proportions as a monthly trend analysis, the achievement of continuous improvement could be easily monitored. Listings of individual cases which did not meet the targets allowed improvements to be made through changes to processes, protocols and provision of training.

Training and development

If the information is to be used and used appropriately, it is necessary to develop an information culture within the hospital. That is, a culture where:

- Information is actively sought to assist in the decision-making process.
- The use of information is valued and encouraged throughout the hospital.
- Requests for change are based on 'business' requirements and present logical arguments which are supported by information.
- Regular, monthly monitoring of information is just one example of 'how this hospital is managed'.

An information culture starts at the top of the organisation. If senior clinicians and managers do not value and use information as part of their decision-making process, then no one else will.

This implies that the training and development programme should not only cover what information is available and how it can be used but also that information should be part of the hospital's overall organisational development programme. Information should be on the agenda for every manager's continuing development programme. All new management staff should understand what information is available, how it can be used and what support is available, as part of their induction programmes. Information should be on the agenda of all first, middle and senior management training courses.

Training products and courses

There are a range of training products and courses available from basic information awareness to Masters in Medical Informatics.

The NHS Training Directorate is supporting the development of a nationally recognised qualification for information staff in the NHS. Drawing on previous work at diploma and masters' level at Aberystwyth, Loughborough and Manchester universities, a new qualification is aimed at certificate level.

The directorate has also developed a number of products to improve awareness including an Executive Information Systems Demonstrator[38] and LEARNIT,[39] a computer aided learning package for managers.

Training in the use of a particular Casemix Management system is generally provided by the supplier of the system.

HERMES

One training package in particular deserves more detailed description. HERMES[40] was developed by the Resource Management Unit of the NHS Executive to help users of Casemix Management systems to understand the information available and how it can be used, while developing the information culture of the hospital. HERMES (Hospital Environment Resource Management Educational Simulator) evolved from an original idea by the author.

In early 1990, a number of workshops were held with sites who that were beginning to use casemix information and were beginning to see some benefits from it. The aim was to determine what would speed up the process of gaining expertise in the use of the information from casemix in order to benefit hospitals on the programme.

The aim was to develop a package that senior managers would want to use and which would develop technical information skills as a by-product of use of the information. Participants would need feedback on their use of information in the decision-making process. HERMES was born.

HERMES is based on a computer system which simulates a hospital and its Casemix Management system. Using associated workbooks, the participants work through a series of decision-making exercises. After viewing the information about what is happening in the hospital, decisions are made. These decisions are then implemented in the system and the hospital starts admitting, treating and discharging patients. The results of the decisions can be seen after the hospital has been operating for up to a year.

HERMES provides a safe environment in which to try out decisions. It provides the type of information that can be provided by any Casemix Management system that conforms to the core specification. Discussion of local issues is inevitable and encouraged in the group working.

The program can be run as a self-teach package or supported by internal training staff. Perhaps maximum benefit can be obtained in the shortest timescale by using external consultants to support the program: consultants who are expert in the use of information to manage hospitals and have a detailed knowledge of the HERMES package.

Information skills

Casemix systems should be implemented in such a way that users do not need any great skill in using computers to be able to obtain the information that they require, when they require it. However, in order to maintain a system that is responsive to users' needs, some staff in the organisation, probably within the Information department, will need to develop skills in the use of the reporting tools used in order to be able to set-up and maintain views and reports for the users. These staff will not only need to be skilled in using the particular reporting tools which are part of the system but will also need to understand information, how it can be analysed and presented and how it should be interpreted.

A wide range of different tools are used on different Casemix Management systems, and training in their use is normally provided by the supplier of the tools themselves rather than the casemix system supplier.

Training in the use of information has often been poor in the NHS. Very often, talented enthusiasts have been recruited to these posts and have undertaken their own development as best they could. Health Service Management Units at Birmingham and Manchester have run short programmes on aspects of Medical Informatics which are particularly valuable. There are now several centres that run Masters' courses in Medical Informatics to ensure better training of key staff for the future. A certificate programme is also available.

The Resource Management Unit and the NHS Training Directorate have developed or sponsored the development of a number of training products which can help in the area of information use.[38, 39, 41, 42]

Appendix A. Further reading and training packages

Further reading

Guidance on Clinical Directorates. Central Consultants and Specialists Committttee, British Medical Association. 1990.

Models of Clinical Management, S.Disken, M.Dixon, S.Halpern, G.Shocket. The Institute of Health Services Management. 1990.

Step by Step Guide to Producing and Using Profiles. Resource Management Unit, NHS Management Executive. (1992)

Costing for Contracting. National Steering Group on Costing, NHS Management Executive. (1993)

Diagnosis Related Groups in Europe. Uses and Perspectives. Edited by M.Casas, M.M.Wiley. Springer-Verlag. (1993)

DRGs A guide to grouping and interpretation. Linda Jenkins, Martin McKee, Hugh Sanderson. CASPE Research. (1990)

DRG Experience in England 1981-1991. Toni Newman, Linda Jenkins. CASPE Research.

Training packages

HERMES. A complete training package comprising a computer simulation of a hospital and its management information system and workbooks. Quality Clinical Management, NHS Management Executive.

Clinical Coding. A computer-based training course. Training Directorate, NHS Management Executive.

Grouping Patients for Doctors and Managers. A computer-based training course. Training Directorate, NHS Management Executive.

LEARNIT. NHS Management Executive Training Directorate. 1991.

Executive Information System Demonstrator. Training Directorate, NHS Management Executive.

Appendix B. Calculating variation

Variation may be calculated in many ways, each giving slightly different information. The calculations for total, volume and process variation accumulate the variation between the individual patient's records and that expected for the corresponding patient group over the categories required for the specified report.

The following provide a set of variation calculations.

Total variation

Total variation is the difference between the expected number of patients and what was expected to happen to them and the actual number of patients and what in fact happened to them.

Σ Groups ((Act.# patients * Act. Process Cost) - (Exp.# patients * Exp.Process Cost))

Total variation = Volume variation + Casemix variaton + Treatment variation

Volume variation

Volume variation is that element of the total cost variation which is explained by the different number of patients being treated.

Σ Groups ((Total Act.# patients - Total Exp.# patients) * Average Exp.Treatment Cost)

Casemix variation

The casemix variation is the element of total cost variation which is explained by the different type or mix of patients being treated.

Σ Groups (Exp.Cost of Treatment * (Act.# patients - (Total Act.. # patients/Tot.Exp.# patients)))

Treatment variation

Treatment variation is that element of the total variation in costs due to the fact that patients experienced different health interventions and events from those which were expected.

Σ Groups ((Act.# patients * Act.Treatment Cost) - (Act.# patients * Exp.Treatment Cost))

Illustrations of variation are given using the example of eight hypothetical patients from two casemix groups.

Expected numbers and cost

	Group 1	Group 2
Expected number of patients	10	2
Expected cost per case	£500	£300

Actual patient records

Patient id.	Cost	Group
1	£500	1
2	£400	1
3	£400	1
4	£350	1
5	£450	1
Subtotal	£2,100	
6	£250	2
7	£250	2
8	£320	2
Subtotal	£820	

Variation calculations

Total variation   = (((500+(2x400)+350+450)-(10x500))+((2x250)+320)-(2x300))
                       = - 2,680

Volume variation   = ((5-10) + (3-2)) x (((10*500) + (2 x 300)) / 12)
                       = - 1,867

Casemix variation   = (500 x (5-(8 x (10/12))))+(300 x (3-(8 x (2/12))))
                       = - 333

Treatment variation   = ((500+400+400+350+450)-(5x500))+((250+250+320)-(3x300))
                       = -480

Appendix C. Minimum data set

The following list gives inpatient data items and is modified from that in the minimum core specification published by the Resource Management Unit of the NHS Management Executive in January 1989.[2] It has been updated to reflect changes necessary following publication of the NHS White Paper, *'Working for Patients'*.[43]

Category	Item	Priority
ALL PATIENTS		
Contract details	Contract identifier	Essential
Patient details	Date of birth	Essential
	District of residence	Essential
	GP	Essential
	NHS number	Essential
	Patient identifier	Essential
	Patient's name	Essential
	Sex	Essential
Diagnostic event (e.g. Pathology test)	Date of test / request	Essential
	Nature of test / request	Essential
	Result*	Desirable
Therapeutic event (e.g. Physiotherapy)	Date of procedure	Essential
	Nature of procedure	Essential
	Result*	Desirable
Operative procedures	Actual date of procedure	Essential
	Planned date of procedure	Essential
	Consultant performing procedure	Essential
	Duration of procedure	Desirable
	Location of procedure	Essential
	Nature of procedure	Essential
Encoding / Grouping	Admitting diagnosis	Desirable
	Principal diagnosis	Essential
	Secondary diagnoses	Essential
	Principal procedure	Essential
	Secondary procedures	Essential

* Result is intended to indicate normality or abnormality, not to give the full numerical or textual result of a diagnostic or therapeutic event.

Category	Item	Priority
INPATIENTS		
Provider spell details	Start date	Essential
	Source of admission	Essential
	Indented management	Desirable
	Duration of elective wait	Desirable
	Discharge destination	Essential
	Discharge method	Essential
	Discharge date	Essential
	Discharge ready date	Desirable
	Reason for retention	Desirable
	Readmission indicator	Desirable
Consultant episode details	Episode number	Essential
	Consultant	Essential
	Specialty	Essential
	Start of episode date	Essential
	End of episode date	Essential
	Diagnoses	Essential
	Operative procedures	Essential
	Diagnostic events	Essential
	Therapeutic events	Essential
Home leave	Date on home leave	Essential
	Date of return	Essential
Ward details	Ward code	Essential
	Ward episode start date	Essential
	Admission source	Essential
	Ward episode end date	Essential
Nursing time*	Date / shift / day	Essential
	Dependency category	Essential
	Planned qualified hours	Essential
	Planned unqualified hours	Essential
	Actual qualified hours	Essential
	Actual unqualified hours	Essential

* The data items for nursing time will tend to vary depending on the operational systems installed to provide the data. The data items shown, indicating the level of resources used per patient per day, might be expected where a nursing dependency system is in use.

Category	Item	Priority
OUTPATIENTS		
Attendance details	Clinic identifier	Essential
	Consultant	Essential
	Specialty	Essential
	Attendance date	Essential
	Attended / did not attend	Essential
	Problems / symptoms / diagnoses	Essential
	Operative procedures	Essential
	Diagnostic events	Essential
	Therapeutic events	Essential
	Care stage	Desirable
ACCIDENT & EMERGENCY PATIENTS		
Attendance details	Attendance classification	Essential
	Initiator of referral	Desirable
	Type of accident classification	Desirable
	Arrival mode classification	Desirable
	Method of departure classification	Essential
	Attendance date and time	Essential
	Departure date and time	Essential
	Problems / symptoms / diagnoses	Essential
	Operative procedures	Essential
	Diagnostic events	Essential
	Therapeutic events	Essential

Appendix D. Bibliography

[1] Conceptual Framework for Clinical and General Management, Bullas, Kwo, Lowson and Sanderson. Proceedings of the twelfth International Congress of the European Federation for Medical Informatics (MIE 94), May 1994.

[2] Casemix Management System Core Specification. NHS Management Executive Resource Management Unit. January 1989.

[3] Casemix Management System Survey, Version 4. Quality Clinical Management, NHS Management Executive. 1994. (Confidential to NHS).

[4] Guidance on Clinical Directorates. Central Consultants and Specialists Committee, British Medical Assocation. 1990.

[5] Models of Clinical Management, S. Disken, M. Dixon, S. Halpern, G Shocket. The Institute of Health Services Management. 1990.

[6] Healthcare Resource Groups. National Casemix Office, Information Management Group, NHS Management Executive. 1993.

[7] A new format NHS number. An IM&T Strategy for the NHS in England. Information Management Group, NHS Management Executive. December 1992.

[8] Clinical Coding. A computer-based training course. Training Directorate. NHS Management Executive.

[9] International Classification of Diseases, Injuries and Causes of Death: Manual of the International Statistical Classification of Diseases, Injuries and Causes of Death: 9th revision. WHO. 1977.

[10] Classification of Surgical Operations and Procedures. 4th Revision. OPCS. 1987.

[11] International Classification of Diseases. 9th revision. Clinical modification. US National Committee on Vital and Health Statistics. 1980.

[12] READ codes. National Centre for Coding and Classification, NHS Management Executive.

[13] What are the Read Codes? An IM&T Strategy for the NHS in England. Information Management Group, NHS Management Executive. December 1992.

[14] The Classification and Analysis of General Practice Data, 2nd edition. Royal College of General Practitioners. 1986.

[15] Oxmis Problem Codes. Oxmis publications. 1978.

[16] Anatomical Therapeutic Chemical (ATC) Classification Index. WHO Collaborating Centre for Drug Statistics Methodology. January 1992.

[17] Clinical Coding Toolbox. Resource Management Unit, NHS Management Executive. 1991.

[18] DRGs and health care, the management of casemix. Ed. Bardsley, Coles and Jenkins. King Edward's Hospital Fund for London.

[19] DRGs - A guide to grouping and interpretation. Linda Jenkins, Martin McKee, Hugh Sanderson. CASPE Research.

[20] DRG Experience in England 1981-1991. Toni Newman, Linda Jenkins. CASPE Research.

[21] Parkin D. et al. A comparison of DRGs and AVGs in day case surgery. Health Trends. 1993.

[22] Grouping Patients for Doctors and Managers. Training Directorate, NHS Management Executive. 1989.

[23] The product of a hospital. Codman E.A. Surgery, gynaecology, obstetrics, 18: 491-496. 1914.

[24] Hospital cost variation and casemix differences. Feldstein M.S. Med. Care 3: 95-103. 1965.

[25] Contract Categories Report. National Casemix Office, NHS Management Executive, April 1993.

[26] Maintaining high quality patient care while controlling costs. Batchelor & Esmond. Healthcare Financial Management. February 1989.

[27] Proceedings of Total Quality Management Conference. Intermountain Health Care, Salt Lake City, Utah. 1993.

[28] Resource Management Health Notice (86)34. NHS Management Board. November 1986.

[29] Implementing DRGs in Portugal: a summary of the first real European experience. Proceedings of the 6th international PCS/E working conference, Saint Etienne. Bentes M. 1990.

[30] Implementation of DRGs for financing hospitals in Norway. Proceedings of the 7th international PCS/E working conference, Lausanne, Hogsnes T. 1991.

[31] Hospital comparison using a Euro health database for resource management and strategic planning. Roger France F.H. et al. Health Policy 17: 165-177. 1991.

[32] European Reference Model for the Development of Open Information and Communication Systems for Hospitals. Prof. Dr. Albert van de Werff, Hubert Mensch, Anton Kilsdonk. August 1991.

[33] Diagnosis Related Groups in Europe: Uses and Perspectives. Ed. M. Casas, M.M. Wiley. Springer Verlag. 1993.

[34] Department of Health: Development of a Classification System for Outpatients. CSL. March 1990.

[35] Costing for Contracting. EL(93)26. NHS Management Executive. April 1993.

[36] Costing and Pricing Contracts. Cost Allocation Principles. NHS Management Executive. October 1990.

[37] Cost allocation general principles and approach for 1993/1994. NHS Management Executive. February 1993.

[38] EIS Demonstrator Software. NHS Management Executive Training Directorate. 1992.

[39] LEARNIT. NHS Management Executive Training Directorate. 1991.

[40] HERMES Training Pack. NHS Management Executive, Resource Management Unit. November 1991.

[41] IMT Training for Managers. NHS Management Executive, Training Directorate. 1991.

[42] IMT Training Solutions in the NHS - Case Studies. NHS Management Executive, Training Directorate 1991.

[43] *Working for Patients* White Paper. HMSO. 1989.